Praise for *The Healer's Path*

MW00564912

"I have no doubt that readers will find meaningful and healing truths that penetrate below the bedrock of language in this book, reach into the roots of their Tree of Life, and nourish each branch of their body, soul and life."

–Bernard Ewigman, MD, MSPH, FAAFP, Owen L Coon Chair of Family Medicine, North Shore University Health System, Clinical Professor, University of Chicago Pritzker School of Medicine

"A special book that can help anyone chart a path through difficult times and emerge stronger, better, and more soulful."

–Wayne M. Sotile, PhD, Author of *Thriving in Healthcare* and *The Thriving Physician*

"An essential toolkit for healthcare providers seeking restoration from the corrosive consequences of the pandemic in their personal and professional lives. Written with the wisdom and compassion of an experienced healer and guide, it is a roadmap for radiant living, even within the depths of trauma and tragedy. Dr. Kelly's application of her Soul Health Model to the unique needs and circumstances of healthcare providers is a vital contribution to post-pandemic healthcare."

– Joseph Biggs, PhD, Psychologist

"Dr. Kelly's book provides solace and insight into the professional lives of health care providers during this historic pandemic. The stories shared throughout the book reveal the common experience of health care providers. You will feel heard and acknowledged. Her guidance for healing and recovery is an invaluable resource to embrace and grow from the lessons of the pandemic. A must read."

–Lea Harrell Kirkland, MD, Psychiatrist

"*The Healer's Path to Post-COVID Recovery* validates what many health-care providers experienced during the COVID pandemic. Dr. Kelly has provided an insightful guide to healing the deepest areas of the soul that were severely impacted by this pandemic. She then takes it a step further to help you recognize the complex feelings that reside deep within you to transform the darkest hours into the brightest light!"

–Briana L. Garcia, RN, LMBT

"Drawing from the personal experiences of close to one hundred traditional healthcare workers navigating the frontlines of a pandemic, Dr. Kelly takes the reader to the core of our collective despair and trauma, then guides the journey back, calling on our innate resilience through the art and skill of soul work healing. This book is a MUST READ to start the healing journey."

–Barbara Bennett, MSN, RN,CEO, Pavillon
Residential and Outpatient Treatment Services

"As a pharmacist, I can relate to the healthcare stories in this book. I have felt the uncomfortable truth of not having all the answers for customers as well as regulatory boards changing regulations at never before seen frequency. This book was like a lifesaver thrown to a sinking soul."

–Elizabeth D. Marley, Pharm D

"Dr. Katherine Kelly provides a powerful blueprint for healing and moving beyond the stress and trauma of the COVID-19 pandemic. This book offers insight into learning how thrive and shine our light as a beacon for others better than we could imagine. It's a roadmap for personal evolution, not just in the aftermath of COVID, but for other dark times that we all inevitably experience."

–Melissa Curran, Certified Aromatherapist,
Holistic Life Coach and Reiki Practitioner

"*The Healer's Path* is a guide to see beyond your darkened path and into the healing light of the dynamic horizon of the soul. This book will illuminate and awaken your higher self by examining the branches of The Soul Health Model."

–Dr. Blake Kovner, ND, LM

"Dr. Katherine Kelly's words give voice to many of the thoughts, struggles, and emotions that I, as a physician assistant on the front lines of the COVID-19 pandemic, have felt but not had the capacity to process fully. However, she does not allow that voice to stir up pity or dwell in the past. She acknowledges the darkness and uses it as a springboard for hope and a way forward. This book is a much needed blueprint to get you back to a brighter future."

– Jennifer Nall, MPH, MMS, PA-C

"Katherine T. Kelly, Ph.D., has created an invaluable resource for the healthcare workers of this country and the world. She very eloquently explains the journey that has impacted this industry and its practitioners so severely through her interviews. She then provides the pathway with tools for healing and restoring the essence or soul which has been lost. I highly recommend her book for all healthcare and 'soul care' practitioners who have been impacted by the COVID-19 pandemic and these chaotic times."

–Kate Olson, CHT, CPC, Author of *Living In Joyful Resilience*, Speaker, Radio Host, Life Coach, Hypnotherapist, NLP & Reiki Practitioner

"I was struck by the shared journey that all of us in the helping professions have gone through. This time has certainly been exacerbated by the isolation that many of us felt. As a mental health professional in private practice, isolation from friends and colleagues and the needs of my clients has been overwhelming. Once I read this book, I did indeed find a light at the end of the tunnel with her wise insights and protocols to heal all the branches of our lives. This book provides physical, emotional and spiritual ways to heal ... and learn from all we have been through so that we truly evolve. I will be recommending this book to all my colleagues."

–Cheryl Rubin, MSW, LCSW

"Dr. Kelly shows the most devastating effects that Covid has had on healthcare workers on the front line of this war. She shares input from healthcare workers that she interviewed and brings light and awareness to this situation. Dr. Kelly's book offers insight and solutions for individuals to work through the healing process while guiding them to grow and evolve at soul level. This book will help provide restoration and rebalancing in all of our lives."

–Carol Downey, RN, BSN, Maternal/Child and Newborn ICU provider, Clinical Adjunct Professor, Oklahoma City Community College

"As health care workers, we have been flooded with our own narrow, sometimes harrowing, experiences of the pandemic. It has been hard to truly grasp the scope of this suffering. Dr. Kelly has deftly woven these glimpses into a cohesive whole, giving us the opportunity to process this shared experience, shed our forced isolation, and open ourselves to the spiritual growth that will surely follow, if we let it."

–Dr. Susan K. Burden, MD, Specialized Ophthalmology

"*The Healer's Path to Post-COVID Recovery* is a welcomed tool for healthcare workers trying to navigate the healing process of trauma caused by working in an unprecedented pandemic. Dr. Kelly's expertise and skill set poised her to provide this timely resource. I highly recommend it to anyone in the healthcare space looking for help along their journey to peace."

–Beth Buie, MMS, PA-C

THE
HEALER'S
PATH
to Post-COVID
Recovery

A
Restorative
Journey for
Healthcare
Workers

THE
HEALER'S
PATH
to Post-COVID
Recovery

Dr. Katherine T. Kelly
PHD, MSPH

SOUL HEALTH
PRESS

Soul Health Press
www.soulhealthpress.com or www.drkatherinetkelly.com

Because of the dynamic nature of the Internet, any web addresses or links contained in this book may have changed since publication and may no longer be valid.

The author of this book does not dispense medical advice or prescribe the use of any technique as a form of treatment for physical, emotional, or medical problems without the advice of a physician, either directly or indirectly. The intent of the author is only to offer information of the general nature to help you in the quest for emotional and spiritual well-being. In the event you use any of the information in this book for yourself, which is your constitutional right, the author and the publisher assume no responsibility for your actions.

ISBN (paperback): 978-1-7320489-6-6
ISBN (hardcover): 978-1-7320489-7-3
ISBN (ebook) : 978-1-7320489-8-0

Cover and interior design by Christy Day, Constellation Books

Library of Congress Control Number: 2021923008

Printed in the United States of America

To the healthcare forest of the world.

CONTENTS

Like tiny seeds with potent power to push through tough ground and become mighty trees, we hold innate reserves of unimaginable strength.

–CATHERINE DEVRYE

ACKNOWLEDGMENTS

Trees give us life. We literally wouldn't survive without them. Now they provide the metaphor for us to also thrive. I'm grateful for the magic of their roots, trunks, bark, branches and leaves. These magnificent beings, my teachers, role models, friends and family are my life and I am both blessed and humbled to live among you. I learn from you every day.

I'm honored to thank the millions of healthcare workers who represent the world's healing forest. Without you we would not survive nor would we thrive. I have had the privilege of knowing many of you and it is gratifying to be of assistance on your healing journeys. As a result, I have been gifted with a unique opportunity to evolve. I am forever grateful for the wisdom you have shared directly or I have observed as I witnessed your evolution.

My deep gratitude goes to the many authors, teachers, philosophers, health educators and practitioners, spiritual teachers and leaders, arborists, botanists and naturalists, whether in this world or beyond, whose wisdom facilitates and informs my own evolution. Your knowledge allows me to advance the evolution of others – a gift I greatly welcome, integrate, translate and humbly deliver.

Fortunate is a soul whose connections are meaningful, mutually necessary and feed one another's being. Throughout the writing of this book, I've been blessed by the ongoing connections I've held for years and even lifetimes. As a result of this project, I've also been fortunate to reconnect with several influential souls from my past. This proves that tragedy can, indeed, bring many blessings.

It is a true and cherished blessing when two souls connect, remember and recognize a shared and sacred bond—one that is to be nurtured, protected and respected. You know who you are. This book would not have been transcribed in its essence without the profound impact you've made on my life. Your spirit is an immense gift to me and to the readers who will benefit from the words held within the cover. My deepest gratitude goes to you from the beginning to the end of time.

Special thanks goes to Carol Hildebrandt, medical editor, chief word-smith and concept cheerleader who stepped in once again to fine-tune the words on these pages. Your swift work and expertise is priceless!

Continued thanks go to Chara Murray, my graphic genius and friend who gets me, supports my adventures and has somehow pictorially captured the various abstract goings on in my head. You're amazing and very much appreciated as part of my own soulful path. Just so you know, we're not done yet.

To all of the beings who make up my soul's forest, please receive my words as a reminder that you are treasured, honored, and very much appreciated. You feed me at the deepest level possible and I am grateful from the depth of my soul to the furthest reach in the Universe.

Finally, my gratitude goes to everyone who reads this book. Whether you are a healthcare worker, a helpful, supportive loved one, an administrator or supervisor who wants the real scoop on how to help your employees or anyone else that the following words assist, I am grateful. All of you contribute to creating a healing forest, one that will rise above COVID-19.

Light and love goes to each soul who can benefit from this book in some way. It is not enough to heal. We must evolve *beyond*.

A NOTE FROM THE AUTHOR

When I contacted a literary colleague about writing this book, it was just eleven months into the pandemic. Having worked closely with her on the revision of my first book as well as suggesting I write my second, she immediately gave a resounding and definite "Yes!" She knows my work well and also knows my passion to help, heal, educate and elevate others. This time it is you, healthcare practitioners, who need a path to heal.

Within a few weeks of our conversation I had connected with friends, colleagues, mentors, clients—both former and current, acquaintances and many I did not already know—all of whom work or have worked in healthcare. Few declined to contribute because, of course, they as professional helpers like you, wanted to participate in helping me help others heal from this life-altering—and sometimes life-shattering—experience. Since then, I've interviewed nearly one hundred traditional healthcare providers throughout the United States and Canada—nurses (intensive care, traveling critical care, public health, cardiac, trauma, emergency and primary care), physicians (emergency medicine, infectious disease, internal medicine, family medicine, oncology as well as general, thoracic, trauma and ophthalmology surgeons, obstetricians, gynecologists, optometrists, and dentists), nurse practitioners and physician assistants from various fields within healthcare, nursing home directors, emergency medical technicians (EMTs), paramedics, administrators of residential substance abuse centers, psychologists, social workers, psychiatrists, employee assistance therapists, physician wellness coordinators, physical therapists, nutritionists, recreation therapists, nurse anesthetists, hospital administrators, medical school administrators and faculty, medical students and residents, and more.

I've also interviewed dozens of holistic practitioners such as integrative physicians, chiropractors, naturopathic physicians, massage therapists and other body workers, health coaches, herbalists, aromatherapists, homeopaths, reflexologists, energy medicine practitioners, acupuncturists, and yoga and Pilates instructors. In several cases, I spoke with spouses, adult children or parents of healthcare workers, all giving a different perspective from loved ones during the interviews. I've even spoken with veterinarians, who also saw a huge rise in illness among the animals they treat, some likely due to absorbing their owner's pandemic-related stress.

I spoke with men and women within each field and made sure I interviewed providers of all ages and races in both rural and metropolitan areas. Many shared information about their widely varied upbringings, which helped me to understand how they had decided on a career in healthcare.

Many of these practitioners lost not only patients to the virus, but also friends, colleagues, family members and spouses. Others lost relationships, marriages, friendships and other previous supports mostly due to conflict or differing values that emerged about how to care for oneself or each other. Some contracted COVID themselves, with a handful almost losing their lives. Many experienced salary cuts despite the long hours spent on the job. Many admitted that exercise and healthy eating went by the wayside, while a few acknowledged seeking therapy to maintain and/or get a start on repairing their own mental health. Few felt fully cared for by their workplaces and some left their jobs. Several moved out of their homes early on, while some left later to avoid or minimize conflict that arose. Sex lives tanked and alcohol use and emotional eating patterns skyrocketed. Collegial "coffee talk" in the breakroom disappeared and staffing happened only by phone or "screen". Spiritual support was lost and many came to question or even abandon their faith.

Later in the pandemic, I contacted several of the providers again to hear how their experiences changed with new variants emerging, the introduction of vaccines and new mandates about mask-wearing. The Delta variant brought many new reactions, including compassion expressed by those who had been overwhelmed by the initial wave of the pandemic for those in other parts of the country who were just beginning the experience. Those who supported the vaccine were often met with either resistance or hostility from those who didn't, while those who had concerns for it felt pressured, ostracized or bullied. In some cases, a once unified mission to help others changed to a division of thought and values that dissolved the previously cohesive task.

As I listened, I couldn't help but cry with many during our calls and cried *for* many after we hung up. Many spoke from an emotionally detached perspective, while others openly shared their heart-wrenching stories. Regardless of their delivery, I could feel and see their pain. As a health and spiritual psychologist in private practice who treats many healthcare providers as well as the general public, I've listened to hundreds of hours of overwhelm, exhaustion and raw emotion that accompanied COVID-19's unknown territory. My already busy private practice brought ten to twelve extra clients per week—and like many of you, I rarely turned people away when help was needed.

Colleagues, friends and clients also lost someone close to them due to this unrelenting virus. I watched friends grieve over the loss of jobs, income, relationships, their own health and even their passion and interest in life. I saw some struggle when they couldn't visit family members who had fallen ill or attend funerals if their loved ones lost the battle. I witnessed extreme anxiety in some for fear of contracting the virus themselves, while many suffered from severe isolation when they couldn't interact with friends or family—nor go to the grocery store, hair stylist or connect with other "constants" in their lives.

And yes, I felt all of it myself. I was overwhelmed, exhausted, burned out, questioned whether I should continue the work I do, cried at the end of several very full and heavy days, thought "this is all too much", sat and stared because I had no energy to do anything else. Like many of you, at times I considered even the most basic self-care a burden—not something I like to admit since my second book touted the importance of this health-enhancing concept. I felt the isolation, the concern for what would come both now and in the future, the inconvenience the virus imposed, the loss of beloved travel that always served as my escape, the absence of creature comforts and personal freedom, as well as the frustration about how people have acted—or not acted to care for one another. I worried about friends who have direct contact with the patient population, wondering how long it would be until one of them, too, fell to the virus. I stopped taking my pups to the dog park in case I ran into someone who might not have taken proper precautions.

As a close friend and colleague reflected, this was the first time in history that we, as healthcare providers, experienced everything that our clients did at exactly the same time and place. The difference was that we were caring for those people as well. For the first time, we had to hold it together to help hold others up, despite our own parallel, faltering condition.

But through the darkness, I saw light.

Although I didn't know how I would muster the energy to write this book, I became strangely and increasingly energized with each interview I completed. I knew I could help and this breathed new life into me, creating both a vision and a mission for how to help others move out of the darkness and into an even brighter future, although many won't initially believe this can happen. And many won't know what hit them until they see the dark clouds moving distant in the rearview mirror, whenever that might be.

Along with hearing the suffering experienced by those in healthcare, I had the privilege of hearing the endless stories of strength, courage, compassion and determination to stick with it to make a difference. In most cases, it wasn't even an option to stop, quit or throw in the towel, even in the hardest and most tragic of caregiving situations. Most providers I interviewed said they were made for their jobs and wanted to do anything they could to help even a few survive.

I also heard many stories about what fellow providers did to support and cheer each other on through the darkest of days. Several described how they became close friends with colleagues they barely knew prior to arrival of the virus, leaning on one another through their shared tragedy since they didn't have to explain to the other what they had experienced. They just knew.

As I heard and watched many let down their guard to share their deepest thoughts and feelings, I felt admiration in knowing that every single person I interviewed gave it their best—often their all—to play a part in this historic event, even if they didn't feel they had contributed much in the least. They gave the best part of themselves through hope that they would give someone else another chance at doing the very same. Few wanted praise for actions; they only wanted the acknowledgement from others of what they had been through. They didn't need those around them to completely understand—they just wanted others to cut them some slack for no longer shining their light fully.

And now it is time to rebuild. It is time to find and reclaim your inner light on your own path to healing.

These are unknown times but we don't have to continue without an identified route. I've written *The Healer's Path to Post-COVID Recovery* to provide a hopeful pathway—the light at the end—that you will come out of this unchartered era renewed, restored and elevated. You've spent your careers helping others. And now it is time for me to help you.

Sixteen years ago, I created a "whole health" model, providing a blueprint or roadmap, to empower those who needed to rebuild or rebalance their lives from daily stressors, trauma, crises or any other challenges faced within the human condition. The model is based on my main premise that it is not enough for me to help others to heal; instead, I want to help them to *evolve*. It is my nature and my mission to help individuals not only restore themselves to previously known health, I strive to elevate them beyond what they once knew and help them get to know themselves in such a way that they will never lose their light again.

In the early development of the model, I realized that something was missing. Something deep at the core of our experience had to be acknowledged and touched in order to heal—we have to heal the very essence of who we are in order to both grow and thrive beyond our fractured and even broken human condition. Traditional therapies often fail to reach this deeper level of healing. So, I started referring to my blueprint as the *Soul Health Model*—to address the *core* of who we are—the essence or "light" that drives us forward even when the circumstances of our human condition tries to snuff us out.

For healthcare practitioners, it is this essence that has been so deeply impacted under the conditions we have experienced since the pandemic first began. There is no way your deepest self has been left untouched. Your own "essence" has been altered, whether you know it yet or not. And once you are ready to rebuild and heal beyond the darkness of these unforgiving days, you will have a blueprint to get you back to a brighter future.

Out of the ten "branches" of the *Soul Health Model*—Physical, Psychological, Social, Interpersonal, Intellectual/Occupational, Environmental, Financial, Sexual, Spiritual and Recreational—none have been left untouched by COVID-19. This pandemic has not only infected us as humans, it has infected both our individual and collective souls—the very essence of who we are as individuals and who we are as a whole. Every aspect of who we are has been touched by this viral demon, leaving deep scars whether visible or not. While actual COVID patients may become long haulers, experiencing residual physical effects from the virus, many healthcare practitioners will be long haulers of a different type—affected by the various "branches" of life that have been touched, fractured or broken from the important role you played in healing others. Your essence has been changed without invitation.

As a whole, the very soul of healthcare has been fractured, and that soul is you. You are the soul of healing. We will never be the same, but whether you can see the light or not, we *can* be even better than we were before this viral enemy arrived.

As a former medical school faculty member, I'm aware that practitioners have a protocol or procedure for everything but themselves. Now, you, our medical and health-related caregivers need to see that there is a path not only back to the pre-pandemic *you*, but there is the possibility of something even brighter beyond the darkness.

One of the most heartwarming and inspirational stories I heard came from an interview with the Chief of Emergency Medicine at NorthShore University Health System in Chicago. When asked what he wanted to remember from this challenging time, he shared with me that although he often saw the beginning of a COVID patient's journey as they were admitted through his department, he rarely knew how their story ended. When his institution began playing the Beatle's song "Here Comes the Sun" as a COVID patient was discharged from the hospital, it brought instant light to his day. The image created by this song offered him hope that the patient who was leaving the hospital was one of those he had treated on their way in.

My earlier book, *Soul Health: Aligning with Spirit for Radiant Living*, offered a blueprint to enhance and heal a person's inner light beyond what they once thought possible. I've taught the model to hundreds of healthcare practitioners around the country through continuing education workshops as well as events offered to the public. Now, I want to help you—our soul of healthcare—to reclaim your own light and build a better future by applying this model to your own journey back to health.

The Healer's Path to Post-COVID Recovery provides the tools to create your own personalized procedure or protocol to help you restore and rebalance life following the events of this historic, but darkening episode. It also serves as a practical guide to progressing *beyond* your pre-pandemic life. In this book, you will find a user-friendly metaphor for creating a life-long path to wellness and optimal health as well as useful tools to get you there. This is not just a "how to" book, this is a "how to *evolve*" book—something that will take you beyond what traditional methods can offer. The "protocol" found within these pages will help you heal from the inside out—a much deeper and sustainable route to a better life.

Part One: The Light Beyond, both explores and affirms the challenging—and often treacherous—journey that you, the healthcare provider have been on since the start of the pandemic. Through the interviews I conducted, I've organized and presented the main themes that impacted the soul of healthcare and "normalized" the reactions many of you have had—often in raw form, just as you experienced it. Within the chapters, you will also read about the elements of health unique to healthcare providers that were most impacted, as well as the myth and mystery of self-care.

Part Two: Restoration to Radiance, builds the foundation—or lays the bricks—on your path to healing. This section more fully describes the *Soul Health Model,* along with how each of the ten "branches" of the human condition may have been uniquely affected for healthcare professionals. The interrelatedness of all of the branches is explained to illustrate that if even one branch is fractured or unbalanced, it will have a significant impact on your overall experience of a radiant life. But you will also see that when you work on just one of the key elements of your health, all of your "tree of life" will benefit.

Part Three: The Healing Path, helps you create and implement a realistic plan to rebuild and rebalance your life—the complete procedure and protocol that most helpers lack for themselves. This section offers an example of a "Soul Health Plan" and other exercises to illuminate your newly developed path, as well as offer tips and suggestions for maintaining your new route to healing once you create it. You will learn how to become a steward of your own health and be shown ways to deepen your commitment to caring for yourself in a practical and sustainable way.

Before I go on, I want to offer some suggestions about how to use this book as you learn about and create your path to healing:

1. Observe your own ability and possible resistance to acknowledge that you've been through a lot. While many I interviewed spoke with detachment, it is important to admit your own brightness may have been dimmed through the events of the darkened days. This book will shed more light on this, as well as illuminate your own path to healing.

2. Know that within you is an inherent desire to survive and thrive—you wouldn't still be here if there wasn't. Through the following pages, you will learn to become more conscious of the essence of who you are—the element that drives every thought, reaction and behavior. Once acknowledged, this essence will guide you in realigning your life if you let it.

3. You are not alone. Of the almost twenty-one million other healthcare providers in this country, there are another thirty-eight million around the world who have experienced the tragedy of this historic event as well. Sprinkled throughout this book are the inspirational stories I heard, both so you can relate to the information presented and also to inspire you to find your own light again.

4. Know that you can evolve. You already have, even if you don't know it. It is not enough for me to help someone heal, I want to help them grow beyond where they were and create an even brighter future than one could imagine.

5. Know that you can do more than endure—you can rise above your burdens. This existential promise is both your birthright and your ticket to not just healing, but to healing beyond your challenges, wounds or broken paths.

6. A brighter life is yours if you want it. I use the word "radiant life" because I've yet to find someone who doesn't want to shine their skills, knowledge and essence more brightly. I plan to show you how to accomplish that.

7. As medical professionals, you know that everything has a procedure or protocol. You are no different. But this time it is your own life you will restore. After reading this book, you will have a) more complete insight into what has darkened your life, b) new understanding about why you need to take the steps to realign the "branches" of your human condition and c) the essential tools to create a brighter path for your future.

"If you have knowledge, let others light their candles in it." I have long loved this quote by American journalist, Margaret Fuller. My hope is that the words I offer in this book will provide you with the tools to rebuild, restore and reclaim your own light while also illuminating your path to healing.

In shared and grateful light,

Katherine T. Kelly, Ph.D., M.S.P.H.

PART ONE
RESTORATION TO RADIANCE

Even the darkest night will end and the sun will rise.
—VICTOR HUGO

CHAPTER ONE
FINDING THE LIGHT

Even in the darkest forest, if one looks hard enough,
light can be found through the trees.
—UNKNOWN

Healthcare remains the largest employer in the United States, with nearly 21 million employees. This means that the largest sector of our working public took the biggest and most multilayered hit with the arrival of COVID-19. Women comprise seventy percent of the global health and social care workforce, which placed them at exceptionally high risk of both infection and the range of physical and emotional concerns associated with their role as health professionals and essential caregivers in the context of the pandemic. Even prior to the pandemic, healthcare workers were already known to be at risk for anxiety, depression, burnout, insomnia, moral distress and post-traumatic stress disorder. While a stark increase in chronic stress was apparent following the severe acute respiratory syndrome (SARS) outbreak in 2003, the intense and longstanding stress and trauma of caring for COVID-19 patients not only exacerbated already present factors for poor mental health among healthcare workers, it has also impacted practitioners at a whole new level and depth. It has hit us at the core of who we are, and there is no deeper this damage can go.

By late 2020, healthcare workers who treated COVID-19 patients already showed much higher levels of depression (50%), anxiety (45%), insomnia (34%) and distress (72%) than prior to the pandemic, indicating that the health of healthcare workers was clearly, but inevitably going in the wrong direction. The long-term effect of working in healthcare with respect to COVID conditions will reveal itself over time. One thing is already certain: while you, our healthcare workers—the soul of our country—have been working hard to keep the light shining within your patients, your own light has dimmed and even darkened as a result of the work you signed on to do.

The Dark Night of the World's Soul

In the attitude of silence, the soul finds the path in a clearer light, and what is elusive and deceptive resolves itself into crystal clearness.
—Mahatma Gandhi

The term "the dark night of the soul" is attributed to Saint John of the Cross, who lived and wrote during the late 1500's. He used this phrase to describe his own painful experiences and their significance on his spiritual journey as a Spanish Catholic priest. Now, this term is used to describe a time when life loses its meaning during harrowing periods of our lives. This "darkness" creates a near total eclipse and even a collapse of what we once found familiar and "known". During these times, we often experience a deep sense of confusion, disorientation, complacency and even dismissal that life is worth the effort. What we know as clinical depression tends to accompany the dark night, but the all-encompassing experience of this difficult time eventually serves to break down the many layers of the human condition, leaving us disarmed, bereft and empty. It strips us of our ability to live life as we once knew it and sometimes destroys our interest in living at all.

These dark periods can make us feel like everything is falling apart, fracturing us at a deep level—the essence of who we are. These gloomy times change us and seemingly darken our souls. But, in fact, the dark night also brings an unexpected opportunity to awaken us to a world that is even better than the one we knew. The challenge is for us to move *beyond* the darkness in order to once again find the light. Only then can we see the opening in the clouds that have blocked our view.

John F. Kennedy once inspired us to consider the Chinese symbol for crisis as one that is also used to describe opportunity by saying "The Chinese use two brush strokes to write the word, 'crisis'. One brush stroke stands for danger, the other for opportunity. In a crisis, be aware of the danger—but recognize the opportunity." Unfortunately, his interpretation wasn't quite right. While the Chinese word for crisis does, indeed, translate to "danger", the symbol doesn't exactly mean "opportunity" when it stands alone. Instead, it more directly translates to "a crucial point when something begins to change."

This pandemic—the dark night of the world's soul—marks a crucial point in history when something has changed and will continue to do so from this day forward. In fact, very little will likely remain the same. No doubt, the world will reel from this event for quite some time. From an individual perspective—your own soul's level—it marks a time to take a deeper look within so you can see beyond the darkness to create a life with far more light, even if you don't see or believe it is possible at first glance.

As I mentioned in the Note from the Author, I have interviewed over one hundred healthcare practitioners, allopathic and integrative included, hearing their stories and experiences since the start of the pandemic. Along with wrenching and devastating stories, I also heard stories of incredible triumph, inspiration and motivation to change one's life as well as beautiful stories of love, romance and other dreams that came true even in these shrouded times.

One former client, who happened to be a nurse, related a surprising and sad story that her marriage disintegrated as a result of COVID. At the time I had seen her as a psychotherapy client, she was deeply in love and her marriage seemed more solid and compatible than most.

However, during COVID things changed. Her husband of thirteen years, also a nurse, became distant and while she initially thought it resulted through overwhelm from his work during the pandemic, she later found that he had been having an affair with another traveling nurse he had met along the way. After trying feverishly to make the marriage work, she eventually let go. Much to her surprise, several months later she met someone with whom she related to even more deeply than she did her husband. She now understands this would not have been possible had she not opened herself to the possibility that something good could come from her cloudy days. She found the light in the darkness and moved forward to grow beyond her broken marriage with someone who brought new opportunities for growth and learning. Along with this opportunity came the surprise spark of a new and deeper relationship.

Another practitioner, who is a leader in family medicine, shared that the pandemic brought him to his knees like never before, noting it as an "unusual experience in an overachieving life". Because I shared my *Soul Health Model*, mentioned in the Note from the Author, with all interviewees, he described branch-by-branch how COVID impacted his life. Although among other things he, like many, experienced social isolation, immense psychological stress and a cut in salary, he also acknowledged a renewed interest in fitness and nutrition, tightening bonds with people at work, "phenomenal mental stimulation" as he was reminded why he went into medicine and a deepened interest in pursuing spiritual aspects of health. He made significant changes at work to both lighten his load and redesign his future, while he also became more committed to finding more balance in his previously unbalanced life. He saw glimmers of the light, even when the layers of the human condition had buried him deeply and shaded his view.

Another family physician shared that his way of coping with difficult life events includes looking for the light at the end of the tunnel as well as searching for "stepping stones" along the way. He mentioned looking ahead to future travel, time with friends and family and things he looked forward to learning both before and after retirement. This method helped him through a fifty-year career, even as a practitioner who lost a dear colleague and several elderly patients to the virus.

Many practitioners noted that they rekindled relationships with spouses, relighting pilot lights that were previously dimmed or extinguished. Some even became engaged to their partners and married during the pandemic, creating light when circumstances could have otherwise kept things dark. Others renewed their love for reading, cooking, and creative ventures, as well as picked up new hobbies and added furry creatures to their home—all actions that illuminated an otherwise routine, mundane and darkened day. Several remodeled parts of their homes or moved into new ones, changing and literally brightening their environments altogether. Whatever the method of finding the light, it seems to be an effective way to cope, look within and move ahead.

I often tell clients that we generally don't change something about our lives until we get tired enough of ourselves or our situations. It is then that we begin to make the adjustments necessary to grow beyond our current darkened and mired state. The pandemic may have presented itself as a crisis, but it has certainly also marked the crucial point when many were ready to find and create light in their lives once again—or perhaps for the very first time.

Rediscovering the Eternal Light Within

If there is light in your heart there can be no darkness in your soul.
—Matshona Dhliwayo

Modern societies have forgotten the word "soul" exists, viewing it as the make and model of a car someone drives, something only people who are "out there" discuss or the type of food found in certain southern states. While philosophers and religious orders once readily and openly spoke of this inner light, contemporary language omits the word almost altogether.

When I created my *Soul Health Model*, which will be discussed in more detail in Part Two, I included the soul—what I call our "inner ally"—into the blueprint. Although it is nearly impossible to define, each of us has an inherent wisdom about what we want and need in life in order to experience more brightness—or what I call radiant vitality. We each know what makes us feel alive and what dims or deadens our psyche. Somehow we know when we are *living* instead of just *existing*, something many have done just to get through this challenging time. This sense of "knowing" usually guides us to rebalance our lives when they seem to be falling apart. The problem is, when something has clouded or darkened our view so much—like a global pandemic—it is hard to hear or see our way out.

In the model, I emphasize that the soul is the driving factor behind all aspects of our experiences within the daily human condition, intentionally omitting any reference to organized religion. We are all individuals in the same game trying to figure out how to master the various aspects of living life. My definition of the word simply points out that the soul is the "essence" of who we are and without awareness of this internal light, our human lives can easily become misaligned.

To me, the soul is the nucleus of who each of us are—the core of our existence. I liken it to the pinpoint of light within us that tells us something is right or wrong, whether we choose to listen to that message or not. It is reflected through our "gut" instinct that tells us we are doing something helpful to our own or another's well-being, whether or not we act accordingly. It is also the energetic tie that binds us to each and every other soul—one that creates our universal community. Simply put, the soul is the key not only to our survival, but also to our personal health, well-being and evolution.

As healthcare providers, many of you see the soul more often than the average person. You see a patient's will to survive even when their body is quickly and unceasingly failing. It is also the drive within you that sometimes goes beyond reason to help someone or keep them alive, as well the unseen factor that keeps you going in the middle of a crisis like a pandemic.

Although numerous researchers have studied resilience and will-power, there is no way to measure the strength or nature of a person's soul. It is the source within us that desires to live beyond the pain—the existential part of us that wants to survive and keeps us fighting until our body can fight no more—or until it rallies beyond possibility to bounce back and recover. Somehow the soul sees beyond the discomfort of the human condition.

Many of you saw this with patients who spent up to hundreds of days in the hospital as well as in yourselves as you fixed your sights on keeping them alive. There is an unexplainable and often unstoppable drive to continue even when on a difficult path, regardless of what the state of the human condition may be. It is the light within us that wants to live on beyond the darkness.

The will to live doesn't come from the human body. It comes from something deeper, stronger and more determined. It is a force that doesn't want anything to interfere with its path—something that individuals invisibly but undeniably carry to keep them alive. This is why even the most tragic of accidents, circumstances—and yes, even a pandemic—fail to send many to an almost certain demise. Sometimes the body gives out and that drive goes with it. But we hear story after story about those who shouldn't have lived and nevertheless did. Even you, as healthcare professionals, are often astounded at the will some individuals show in their fight.

Healthcare providers are taught to keep people alive. You go to all lengths and sometimes personal cost, to give that soul a chance to live. You may not know it is your own soul's recognition of another's, but you hold onto the hope that the patient's inner light will provide one last glimmer of strength to get them through. During the pandemic, you've seen the body defy the soul, ending the light held within for far too many.

The truth is, it isn't the fact that you watched so many bodies fail that has traumatized you. Instead, it is the fact that you've seen so many lights go out—fade, then disappear altogether, that has left you in despair. It is the loss of a soul—the essence of who that patient is—that you grieve. The body was simply a vessel you couldn't save or heal.

Many practitioners take an oath when they graduate from their training, what you've really committed to is keeping individual souls alive. When you can't achieve this, you feel like you personally have failed and it dims your own light.

But how does one win against a global pandemic? It all depends on your own inner light and what you do with it moving forward.

Resilience and the Soul

Storms make trees take deeper roots.
—Dolly Parton

Several of the healthcare practitioners I interviewed said they were tired of seeing posters, brochures and webinars provided by their hospitals and medical facilities describing the "keys" to being a resilient provider. To them, these offerings were empty attempts by administrators to cheer on and "care for" the employees who actually do the hard work. But there is something to be said for the strength that comes from within. While I won't write directly about resilience here, I do want to offer a metaphor related to how trees thrive on their own to make a point relevant to your own journey.

When it comes to our woody neighbors, it really is what's under the surface that tells the story of whether a tree will survive and thrive. Peter Wohlleben, forestry expert and the author of *The Hidden Life of Trees: What They Feel, How They Communicate—Discoveries from a Secret World*, offers a surprising but powerful understanding of what goes on beneath the surface.

The beauty we see in trees—the vibrant green and rich bark—are all really the "trash" produced from what happens within. Chlorophyll is actually clear, while the color we see displays how much the tree processes, transmutes and filters to create the best show of what we recognize as the signature beauty of the image we see. When a tree gives its finest display, we may think it is the healthiest one around, but in fact, it is just putting on a good show for what it does with the trash it compiles and composts within its leaves. What we really see is the result of what the tree has been through to remain alive. The tree is resilient for what it must process in order to survive and seemingly thrive, but it also is likely enduring the greatest amount of stress as it processes the unhealthy and undesirable elements around it. It is processing and transmuting the toxins and debris from others—tragedy and raw emotion in human terms—and turning it into something magnificent. Such is human resilience—making something incredible out of the not so desirable factors of the human condition we have experienced. And such is evolution—growing beyond that which we didn't ask for and also that which we might not quite yet believe we can overcome.

The most evolved and resilient souls on this planet are often the ones who have been through the most. They've taken what they experienced, persevered through and processed—whether conscious of this or not— and directed their energy toward both sustaining themselves—hanging on in the biggest and toughest of life's stories—and putting on a good show that offers healing and beauty to sustain others as well.

This does not mean the tree is not struggling, damaged or feeling pain, it simply means the tree has somehow become a master of resiliency—an ongoing student of evolution.

The difference between trees and humans is that we, the healthcare forest of the world, have more conscious processing to do with more palpable and raw emotion involved. When we fall to our knees because of the storms we are dealt, we don't always know how to stand back up. Trees, even if they lean or fall, often continue to provide enough sustenance to themselves and others to nourish one another. They have an inherent drive to adapt to their surroundings and circumstances while simultaneously sending energy to their "broken" or damaged limbs to help their wounds heal. Also, as we now know through the science presented in Wohlleben's book, trees also continue to help those around them, providing sustenance to their seemingly stronger forest friends and mates while somehow remaining alive themselves.

The most resilient healthcare workers may feel they've been cut off at the knees by this pandemic, but the desire is almost always there to find their way back to the light. For those actual trees who are broken beyond repair, they still find ways to nourish others around them, while decomposing and sending nutrients back into the soil. These "decomposing trees" may look rotten as they disintegrate, but they provide fodder—the lessons, the challenges, the debris so to speak, that both force and inspire the growth of others to continue even in their absence. Therefore, in ways, we must thank the fallen parts of the forest—or appreciate our own fallen times—for stimulation of new growth.

How do we take what we experienced from this historic storm of COVID-19 and create a lush and vibrant forest that provides the best show in the light? How do we take the debris and nourish and restore our own tree?

We find our path to healing among the trees.

Your Evolutionary Path

Out of suffering have emerged the strongest souls; the most massive characters are seared with scars.
–Kahlil Gibran

You will hear me speak of evolution throughout this book, emphasizing the need to move and grow beyond your circumstances to reclaim your own inner light. While Darwin once considered survival of the fittest as the key to a flourishing species, he later changed his focus to "those who adapt the best". In order to flourish, we must adapt and grow beyond our conditions. This is what you as healthcare workers have done since the beginning of the pandemic. Something within you—your inner light—drove you to adjust, often on a moment-to-moment basis, surviving the worst of caregiving circumstances to preserve and maintain someone else's light. You didn't just want to save the bodies of those you treated, you wanted to save their souls—the unique and individual light within your patients' bodies which belongs only to them.

This inner source drives us forward to keep us learning, growing and surviving, but what is the prize? The reward is not just to survive our circumstances, but also to evolve beyond them, rising to higher, deeper ground to find what life is really all about.

When I presented the idea for this book to my literary colleague, I not only mentioned to her that the *Soul Health Model* could provide a user friendly "map" to realigning the lives of practitioners, I also mentioned that I felt healthcare providers would recognize that something deep within had shifted, or had even become fractured or broken. I explained to her that many would recognize something deeper had been altered and traditional therapies likely couldn't offer the full tools to rebuild. The essence of who you are cannot be healed by the basics of what most of us know. It is time to heal the soul of who you are and nothing less will do.

Through several interchanges with the leader in family medicine I mentioned earlier, he came to embrace the idea of *Soul Health*, along with many of the guiding principles I share throughout this book.

His words: "I was ready to turn inward. Ready to recover. My willingness to exercise more, improve nutrition, reduce stress and substitute meaningful relationships with virtual connections all failed to carry me through the burden of being a dedicated physician leader. The pandemic has left me on my knees like never before. My own advice, my own protocols and procedures, no doubt allowed me to fulfill my duties and those above the ordinary call of duty, but have failed to keep me healthy. Willing it to be so truly failed me for the first time in my life. I have been cracked open. Humbled. Brought to my knees. Openness to true alignment guided from an inner wisdom, or that tiny portion of cosmic wisdom that 'I' share and carry in this body—trusting my *true self*—I believe that is something like what you mean by soul and is the part that resonated with me. The [concept of *Soul Health*] has hooked me."

John Muir, the Scottish born American naturalist, who was largely responsible for creating Sequoia and Yosemite National Parks to conserve the giant redwoods said, "Between every two pine trees there is a door leading to a new way of life."

Your path to healing can be paved by the glow of your own inner light—your essence, your soul—if you choose to take the steps to get to a brighter day. In the remainder of the book, I will provide the tools, procedures or protocols to get you there.

CHAPTER TWO
FROM RAW TO RIGHT-SIDE UP

There can be no knowledge without emotion. We may be aware of a
truth, yet until we have felt its force, it is not ours. To the cognition
of the brain must be added the experience of the soul.
—Arnold Bennett

To say the least, I heard a lot of raw emotion from the various
healthcare providers I spoke with during interviews for this book.
They often started out in a very subdued and "professional" manner,
and then once they realized I wanted to hear the whole story, many
started dropping "shit" bombs, "f" bombs and any other language
that fit the purpose. Some even called themselves assholes or bitches
when they described who they had become or used that language
to describe others with whom they became frustrated during the
pandemic. Frankly, I appreciated this rawness because it helped me
know how deeply the wear and tear had cut. It was real. Undeniable.
And I could feel it.

There are really no appropriate words to describe what most have
been through and sometimes using strong language is the only method
of displaying what really goes on inside. As a therapist, I've pretty much
heard—and probably said—just about everything anyway. But when you
hear various levels of healthcare providers—even department leaders

and pastoral care professionals—express themselves in this way, you know the pain runs deep.

When I started doing therapy after my training as a counseling psychologist, many of the classic theories and techniques I learned as a student quickly went out the window. I've come to appreciate that I'm not typical in any way, so typical strategies just didn't seem to get to the real stuff. Instead of instructing clients to use the "I feel... when you..." statements most textbooks teach, I would first encourage them to write out or audibly express the raw emotions and statements they *wished* they could say since we tend to experience the feelings behind difficult events at a deep and sometimes cutting way. In my mind, both personally and as a healing practitioner, unless released, we generally store emotions in the visceral way in which we experience them. Without finding a means to express and release these emotions, we get nowhere and only revisit the experiences over and over again. Only when we acknowledge and free ourselves of these feelings and emotions do we actually put them to rest. Otherwise we just pretend they're not there which only serves to prevent both healing and our personal evolution. We can't move on unless we move *beyond* as well.

At the end of this chapter, I share an exercise to help you release these raw emotions. It is one I've used countless times myself and have encouraged many others to use this exercise as well. Releasing the rawness will not heal everything, but it will certainly help clear the path and allow you to find your light again.

Impossible Questions to Definite Answers

There are questions that are not meant to be answered with words.
Some questions take a lifetime to answer.
−J.R. Rim

How does someone ask questions that capture the experiences of a pandemic? Luckily, my psychotherapy skills came in handy and I put together a sample list that I provided to practitioners when they were invited to participate. However, I generally allowed the conversations to flow organically, which encouraged practitioners to share what they found most helpful and important. Even during the first few interviews, I realized the providers needed and appreciated the opportunity to talk freely and many used the time as an outlet to shed some of the emotions they couldn't share elsewhere. They soon realized I had a fair bit of medical experience and knowledge, having worked in three major healthcare institutions as well as various other specialized medical settings. This allowed most of them to let down their guards and open up to share.

Many noted they relied mostly on colleagues to shed the heaviness of their experiences because partners, spouses, family members and friends just could not understand. The healthcare workers didn't have the energy to fully explain the troublesome events of their day, so most declined to talk about their experiences once off the job unless their loved ones worked in medical fields as well. In most cases, those whose partners or spouses were also medical providers were the ones who felt the most supported and many even noted they felt closer to their partners as a result of more frequent conversations during this harrowing time.

I felt immensely honored and grateful by the fact that so many let me in. The emotional mask many wear to get through the day often served as equal safety to the piece of manufactured security they actually wore on their faces. Each offered a different kind of protection. During some lighthearted banter shared with a previous supervisor I interviewed, we joked about the poker faces we had developed over the years. Both of us admitted having mastered the art of shielding others from our own distress at different junctures in life, despite the turmoil that existed within ourselves just under the surface. He was surprised to hear that I was at the tail end of my third major "dark night" at the time we worked together years ago, proving that I had an early start at mastering my own mask of intentional, but safe deception. It was clear that many of those I interviewed had also mastered this skill until given the opportunity to remove their emotionally protective masks.

Throughout this book, you will read about the many anecdotal elements and stories I heard. I want to provide some early insight into the themes of the experiences we shared during these interviews. Below you will find a few of the sample questions I supplied to interviewees. Following each question, I share the common themes and highlights that emerged as I collected the information. I also offer these questions because many with whom I spoke thanked me later for having asked them; the inquiry served as a means to open their thoughts to facilitate their own paths to healing. Most admitted they hadn't even thought about how they would be able to recover later, they were still very much focused on just getting by now.

As you read, please keep in mind that the following paragraphs hold the depths of what healthcare providers have experienced. Although perhaps heavy to read now, it felt important to share these words early, both to help you resonate with what other providers have experienced as well as to educate you, perhaps, for what you don't already know but might suspect.

Nothing about this pandemic has been light, except for what can come out of it along your healing journey. Providing the following information is intended to help your path to healing go from "raw to right-side up"—to help transform and transmute the darkness into light. As a psychologist, I know we need to acknowledge the pain in order to move forward and move *beyond* it. Only then can we find and reclaim the light within.

Question One: How has COVID-19 changed your life (as a professional, person, partner/spouse, parent, friend, citizen or other)?

Although, at first, many respondents didn't really know how to answer this question, most who worked in direct contact with COVID patients soon said their work during the pandemic made them better providers. They noted that they had become even more compassionate toward those they cared for during their long shifts, even if their patience for non-patient connections had grown very short. Countless admitted feeling humbled by the enormity of the tasks they were now expected to perform, many saying that at the beginning stages of the outbreak, they felt completely stripped of all the competency and knowledge they had accumulated up to that point. Both a psychiatrist and a thoracic surgeon openly stated that the Hippocratic Oath they took when they completed their training felt like a complete contradiction to what they were asked to do as things unfolded early on in the pandemic.

Despite reports that many healthcare providers had considered leaving their jobs, only a few of those I interviewed had actually done so. The rest expressed a renewed love and dedication for what they did, which confirmed their original choice in entering their respective fields. Some did admit that although they liked their chosen work, it was the job they disliked—more specifically, what they had observed about their workplace during the pandemic.

Personally speaking, many of those I interviewed said they felt like they had lost themselves in the midst of chaos. Some felt that, together, they lost their personal and professional identities. This came as a result of the toll the pandemic had taken and from instances when practitioners stepped away from their long-term roles. They stepped into others that were either more involved in the care of COVID patients during the pandemic or less so in order to protect themselves or family members. With any identity shift comes destabilization of life as we know it, so the personal lives of many practitioners suffered as well.

An oncologist said, "Medicine is our life and everything else just fits into that life." So, when her department was told to move to telehealth, it shook her world. Not only could she not "put her hands on patients" to feel what was really there, but she also couldn't fully assess how they were doing emotionally beyond the distance of the computer screen. Her specialty in breast cancer became "the most unimaginable thing" as she had to "examine" breasts on camera. She went on to say that COVID also overtook how she managed her mind, explaining it was terrible to know that people who were curable weren't getting the treatment they needed to cure their disease. After only about six years in the field, she had to adjust her idea of who she was, both personally and professionally. She also had to shift perspective on her personal life, as her two young childrens' education suddenly turned virtual. Although her husband took on the majority of homeschooling, she found herself stepping into a supportive role she hadn't expected, especially on top of her already stressful day job.

An employee assistance counselor who works for a major medical institution shared that many of the clients who came to him in the early days of the pandemic were newly graduated nurses who worked in critical or intensive care. He said their stories were all the same—"People were dying who weren't supposed to die, which dismayed these young professionals since they went into the field to save people's lives. The nurses just weren't seeing that." The counselor's work focused on helping these caregivers redefine their identities while helping to heal the repetitive grief they experienced.

Common to everyone, most providers noted their own significant isolation, having to forego social occasions, family vacations or visits home, as well as not being able to attend funerals for loved ones who had passed as a result of COVID, old age or other illnesses. Many reported shifts in relationships, for either better or worse, but several reported complete breakdowns in their other previously supportive ties. Some turned to Zoom cocktail parties and happy hours, but of course, this wasn't the same as a valued in-person connection. In fact, many admitted that by the end of the day, they simply preferred staring at a wall rather than interacting with others in a shallow way.

The loss of physical touch was also a common theme among the healthcare providers I interviewed. Many reported having to move out of their homes to protect their families, which inevitably meant there would be no hugs, kisses or cuddles to comfort them at the end of the day. Often, the only touch these professionals experienced happened when they turned a patient in their hospital bed or took vitals for the hundredth time during their shift. However, many of the providers I interviewed welcomed various new pets into their homes, which likely allowed them to have even more of the unconditional love they needed beyond what they could get from the humans in their lives.

Guilt seemed to be another theme that arose in conversation. Many admitted to "survivor's" guilt—a common reaction to surviving a situation when others did not. This applied to those who saw younger people die of the illness as well as for those who worked in health-related fields with less exposure to COVID. Those who decided to retire or were provided with "buy-out" packages often felt they were abandoning ship, despite encouragement from friends and colleagues.

One ICU nurse from a hospital in Denver, Colorado shared a story early in her interview—something I tried to reframe into a more positive light. Like many, she said she held guilt about the death of one of her first COVID patients. The patient was a ninety-three year old man, whose wife told the unit to do everything they could to save him. As her floor was already sorely understaffed, she worked alone to hook the man up to all of the machines, both to monitor his vitals and sustain his life. He kept reaching for her hand and because she had tasks to complete, she pulled away to hurriedly connect the devices. He coded and subsequently died while she was in the room. When she told me she would never forgive herself for not having been more "present" and compassionate in his last minutes, I asked her if that changed how she worked with other patients moving forward. She said from that point on, she always paused to "be" with patients for at least a few minutes. She strove to recognize they were human beings and not just patients she was trying to save. I urged her to consider that this lesson might have been his final gift to her as she went on to treat other patients. She paused during the Zoom interview to say she hadn't thought of it that way before. Tears flowed for both of us, but we eventually went on to finish our conversation. I could see something shift within her and at least some of her thick layer of emotion seemed to dissolve.

I also spoke with a senior dean of the medical school in which I completed both my fellowship in Family and Community Medicine and Master of Science in Public Health. He was one of my greatest mentors then and proved to be the same as he filled me in on the current goings on within the school, faculty and administration related to COVID.

After catching up on our lives, we agreed to meet periodically throughout the completion of this project. Following a couple of video calls, he admitted he felt more engaged and inspired to take a look at his own life, as he had become re-absorbed by his work after an earlier attempt to retire. He noted feeling energized to rebalance the "branches" of his own life's tree, not having previously had the nudge or method to do so.

Throughout the interviews, I found myself offering suggestions for treatment, anecdotal information that might help, metaphors and themes I share with clients and overall encouragement to determine what these practitioners needed to help them move forward. Even the ones who felt they were broken, were not. I could see a light within them, even if dim, and knew that with their help in writing this book, I could help others see their light as well. My new and unfolding mission was to turn rawness into right-side up.

Question Two: What has been the most difficult adjustment you've had to make due to the pandemic?

Almost immediately, most healthcare workers I interviewed stated that the fear they experienced contributed to their own challenges during the pandemic—they had to adjust to not knowing what they were doing. Because of the uncertain nature of the virus, many were disarmed by the knowledge they once had—or thought they had, not only in treating their patient populations, but also in protecting themselves and their families. After many years of education, healthcare practitioners are expected to be confident in what they do and they are often shunned if they show anything less than complete self-assurance. In the case of a global pandemic, no health professional has the degree, experience or learned intuition on handling this deadly disease. By far, learning they didn't have the answers was the biggest adjustment most healthcare providers said they had to make.

Many had to adjust to the emotional reactions they experienced early on. A psychologist who works in a large, urban family medicine department stated that the reality of the pandemic hit home when her boss wouldn't accept a piece of paper she tried to give him after a meeting. No one knew at the time how the virus was transmitted, but this refusal drove home the gravity of the situation. Others watched coworkers engage in extreme compensatory behavior—shaving their heads for fear that the virus would contaminate their hair, duct-taping the cuffs of shirts and pants to seal out the viral intruder or avoiding eating, drinking or using the bathroom throughout entire shifts to bypass removing protective coverings. Staying open to how others coped also became an adjustment.

Several noted they literally had to adjust to new ways of living as many moved out of homes or lived in garages for their own sake and that of those with whom they shared their space. One practitioner received an "RV for MD's" trailer—a donated camper that was delivered at no cost—so he could decontaminate prior to entering the family home. Some started taking mega doses of vitamins and minerals known to boost the immune system. Many picked up shifts, not because they really wanted a bigger dose of an already difficult situation, but because it was a way to channel their fear and lack of control into something more productive. One practitioner said her family started eating separately from one another because her daughter has an autoimmune illness. A psychiatrist said she worried she would lose her daughter—an ICU nurse who has Rheumatoid Arthritis and works in New York City. She said, "What if I lose this child? I don't know what would become of me."

Others also feared for family members who lived far away, some who were elderly and living in nursing homes, while others had poor health and couldn't get to doctors without assistance. Some practitioners worried about the mental health of their sons or daughters who also worked in healthcare, many living in urban areas that were the hardest hit. Several healthcare providers also saw their young children suffer from increased stress, depression and anxiety, adding fear as to whether their offspring would bounce back once the pandemic was over.

Question Three: What have you found most shocking or frustrating about this time?

This question provided some of the most insightful information in writing this book. It served to stir and release much of the pent-up frustration, anger and dismay that healthcare practitioners had stored since the beginning of the pandemic.

A few said immediately they were shocked that something like a pandemic could actually happen. One physician assistant who worked in pulmonary oncology said she never imagined an event like this could take place in her lifetime. An experienced surgeon said his own disbelief and skepticism led to a wake-up call upon the arrival of the virus. He was newly married, had a young baby and was happily moving into the next phase of his life. Then the pandemic came to the United States and he said, "Oh my God, this is real!" This new awareness came with a surge of fear, mistrust and uncertainty that many others also expressed. Because of the mixed information the medical center constantly received, he said he didn't know who to believe and it became very clear how "flatfooted" medical providers actually were—no preparation, very slow response and much confusion among both coworkers and the administration for which he worked. Soon after the virus was discovered in the United States, he experienced a crushing headache while at work—something that rarely happened to him. Due to the urgent nature of his duties he was told to continue showing up, so he pushed through the discomfort. Later, of course, it was found that headaches were a common symptom of COVID and he was certain he had contracted the virus, probably while on the job. Luckily, neither his new wife nor child seemed to get sick.

Another common theme expressed by many was the shock that personal protective equipment (PPE) was suddenly "disappearing", when practitioners knew hospitals were well stocked just twenty-four hours prior. When rations began, multiple providers said they were instructed to wear the same mask all day, while they knew that the covering is no longer safe once a person comes in contact with an infectious patient. One nurse noted that this rationing caused pandemonium in her unit, exacerbating an already terrifying situation. A psychiatrist expressed rage about how large, wealthy organizations withheld PPE, stating employees were literally told to "suck it up" since they were *all* limited in what they received. A family practice physician said that, at first, he was laughed at for wearing a welder's helmet to work—the only protection he could find; but others soon followed suit when they couldn't access other means of defense against the virus.

Refusal by healthcare providers to treat COVID patients also entered the realm of shock for some. A critical care nurse said it stunned him to see colleagues decline the care of sick patients, hearing many say they'd rather quit their jobs than care for highly contagious individuals. This nurse, who had worked in intensive care for almost fifteen years, couldn't believe that those trained for highly critical situations suddenly excused themselves from their duties. He said, "Entire populations of people are getting sick—how do you just run away from that? We were made and trained for this." A surgeon was also disturbed when he overheard a colleague say they wouldn't perform surgery on a patient because they heard that a family member had a cough.

On the other hand, this *was* a deadly virus. Some providers expressed disbelief that so many were willing to jump right in, regardless of the danger, especially when so ill-equipped.

Beyond the disbelief and skepticism came the stark awareness that the political scene during the pandemic made matters much worse. Almost every practitioner I interviewed commented about how the pandemic had become political, one nurse even stating he heard a coworker say, "The pandemic was fabricated in order to get rid of the President". Another nurse questioned, "Public health is not political. Don't people get that?"

Whether it was frustration about false information related to wearing masks, social distancing or eventually the decision whether or not to receive the vaccine, multiple healthcare practitioners expressed their shock, frustration and even anger and/or rage that science had been dismissed and denied—sometimes both in the medical community and in the public. While a few practitioners I interviewed admitted refusing to get a vaccine until FDA approval was obtained, none reported avoidance of wearing a mask themselves. Providers who work in both rural and urban settings expressed these raw emotions, and most felt they were often exhausted by trying to convince each patient of the importance of taking precautions—if not for themselves, then for the sake of others. One provider even questioned, "What kind of an ass do you need to be to want individual freedom without taking any personal responsibility?" I heard statement after statement that people could be "absolutely uncaring", "unapologetically selfish", "mind-bogglingly belligerent" and "bewilderingly ignorant".

Two paramedics echoed these concerns, but added an experience of anger toward patients who blatantly lied to dispatch when asked if they had the typical symptoms of COVID or whether they had been out of the country in the last few days. Upon arrival at a person's home, one paramedic said a patient admitted he had just returned from the pandemic hotspot of India a few days before the call. He lied to dispatch just so someone would show up to help him.

Many found themselves angry at the authorities as well. A veterinarian I interviewed found herself irate when the Center for Disease Control (CDC) said the public didn't need to wear masks until two months after the virus had arrived in the United States. She was dumbfounded that the "medical leadership" in our country couldn't see what was happening around the world that indicated and proved otherwise.

Many others who worked for both major and regional medical systems expressed their anger and resentment for how their organizations responded as a whole. Several noted twenty- to thirty-percent pay cuts, while being asked to work more hours than ever. These same individuals also lamented the furlough of necessary staff, including other healthcare professionals they desperately needed in order to do their own jobs. Many reported understaffing prior to the pandemic and were completely baffled when their employers decreased staff even more.

For some, this shock and concern stretched to issues of racism, when healthcare providers became concerned that coworkers of color couldn't safely enter hospitals because of the riots going on outside or in other nearby states. One ICU nurse from Manhattan said that the bottom two floors of their facility were boarded up for months out of fear that rioters would infiltrate their boundaries, exposing them to both violence and potential infection.

Another somewhat surprising theme that emerged during the interviews was the frustration with how administration attempted to support or cheer on their employees. At first, many appreciated the gestures, but most providers I interviewed said they later came to resent the "mandatory resiliency training", "hero posters" and other empty nods of support.

One of my final questions to interviewees was, "What do you NOT need in order to recover from this challenging time?" While some couldn't yet think of an answer, many immediately said they don't want to be called a "hero" or to be offered "praise" or "thanks" from their administrators.

Early on, several practitioners said they were taken aback when called "healthcare heroes", mostly because at the time they didn't feel like they knew what they were doing. The initial uncertainty and the confusion about the best medical practices during the pandemic often created a sense of "imposter syndrome"—doubting your abilities and feeling like a fraud, which made the "hero" comments feel all that much worse. An ICU nurse from a large city said "The big thing to know is that we didn't know what we were doing. It feels weird to not be able to run into a room to help someone right away, both because we have to take several minutes to put on our PPE, but also because we don't know what we are getting into until we are in the room. That's not heroic to me." A family practice physician said, "I'm not a hero—I'm terrified to do this work!" Several other practitioners alluded to the same, one saying, "There are lots of people who do their jobs. We are no different."

The dismissal of praise and thanks was much the same, but for different reasons. Most who commented about this felt their hospitals really didn't care much about their well-being and only offered gestures as an obligation or marketing technique to portray a positive image to the community. Few felt their institutions did much more than offer posters and banners as a sign of gratitude. Some commented that when they were "talked up", they actually felt like administrators were talking "down" to them. One provider felt their organization was creating "artificial ways" to thank them but weren't really serious about the offerings. Many providers admitted feeling jaded by how managers handled their schedules, the unavailability of PPE and general lack of concern for the practitioner's overall health.

Most felt that administrators were insulated and unaware of what providers actually experienced while trying to do their jobs. One even said he'd like to see administrators "get out of their sealed offices and put on gowns to work with us for a day". All of the perceived empty gestures by the institutions caused resentment and anger, although most providers admitted they likely wouldn't share these feelings in their workplaces for three main reasons: 1) because they didn't believe anything would change, 2) they remained dedicated to their work and their patient care, and 3) they didn't want to lose their jobs, especially when the future was already uncertain.

There is much research in the field of industrial psychology to support the idea that feeling valued in the workplace leads to the highest levels of employee morale, but in the case of healthcare, overall job satisfaction only seems to have decreased within the worker population since the pandemic began. Hopefully enough administrators will read this book to really understand what employees do and don't need on their path to recovery.

Question Four: What do you want to forget?

As can be expected, two memories from the pandemic were most frequently cited: 1) The multiple "Zoom death videos" many nurses graciously provided to families in the last moments of a patient's life, and 2) the number of bodies a practitioner "bagged" before the end of their shift. One practitioner's wife I interviewed said her husband called her mid-summer of 2020 to tell her he had just put his 100th body in a bag. I interviewed him later to find that he was up to over 300 bodies by the time we spoke. Grief will be more fully discussed later in the book, but needless to say, this will be another area of psychological health that will need much attention.

Enough said.

Question Five: Is there anything you want to remember about this time? What was most heart-warming? Most rewarding?

As I mentioned earlier in this book, it was truly inspiring to speak with so many healthcare providers from around the country and Canada, all ready to share the good, the bad and the ugly of their COVID-19 experiences. Hearing what they wanted to remember from this challenging time only increased my inspiration and appreciation for the soul of our country. These individuals know how to appreciate life when it doesn't seem appreciable at all.

While many didn't want to hear thanks from their workplaces and administrators, many were struck by the gratitude they received from their patients. One practitioner said that in her over thirty years of working as a primary care physician, she had never seen patients react so caringly toward her and her staff. "I never saw that level of gratitude other than on mission trips in other countries". This gratitude from her patients particularly struck her since her employer wasn't showing the same.

Others appreciated the free food that was delivered during the first several months of the pandemic, many noting that the last thing they wanted to do was cook. The practitioner who received the donated camper, acknowledged how helpful this was at a time when he was too tired to even think about other options to keep his family safe. Many appreciated the extra time spent with college-age children who had returned home when schools were closed, noting that they cherished this special time particularly when so much else was uncertain. Parents always prefer to have their offspring close by during dangerous times and this opportunity seemed to be a consistent benefit of nationwide stay-at-home orders.

An emergency nurse, who was particularly overwhelmed and exhausted when we spoke, said that one day early on in the pandemic, her husband organized a neighborhood parade just for her since she had missed one near the hospital while she was hard at work. All of her neighbors greeted her with signs, cheers and noisemakers as she entered the area leading to her home. In describing this gift, I could see the positive effect that resulted and remained even in the memory.

Numerous providers reported the positive impact of how coworkers came together to support one another even among those who may have known each other only in passing. A critical care nurse mentioned that the main thing he wanted to remember were the group hugs his unit established at the end of each staffing. He noted that although early on, the entire staff had to isolate and stay distant when at work, they eventually started to literally lean on one another following their shift huddles. He said, "Even while dressed in all that protective stuff, we still hugged it out". He mentioned how good it felt to just have someone's chin on his shoulder even for a few brief seconds.

Personally, I've never had so many clients ask how I am doing and show concern—even after my mother passed just five years before the pandemic started. Usually very upbeat and positive, my exhaustion must have been apparent to many. I received thank you cards in the mail, extra words of appreciation at the end of a session and frequent positive messages on my professional Facebook page.

One client, an eye specialist, told me several times that she was happy to hear me sound better, with more energy in my voice. Honestly, it was the process of writing this book that got me out of my own raw emotion and turned me right-side up. Interviewing others also motivated me to fully dive into my own self-care once again. As a professional helper, like you, I could now see my next mission. I knew I could offer some tools that would help you turn your own rawness into something more positive for the future. This project energized me, propelling me forward to a chapter in my life I couldn't have predicted would have come from this "viral book". This event has brought me closer to certain friends, has reacquainted me with colleagues as a result of writing this book and has expanded what I can offer to you in order to turn you "right-side up" as well.

My intention now is to help you see the good that can come from this historic event. For many, one important concept gained a new appreciation: the need to practice self-care—something that completely mystifies most healthcare providers. As you come to understand the importance of acknowledging the essence of who you are—your soul—in the process of rebuilding your life, you will be better able to rebalance the branches of health that have become fractured, misaligned or broken. The next chapter will help you explore realistic solutions to both the myth and mystery of self-care.

"Wringing Out the Rawness" Exercise

Researchers clearly report that journaling or venting out emotions on paper is not only effective in releasing unwanted emotion, but also in providing insight for both how the emotions got there and sometimes how to resolve them. Simply put, writing helps you to heal and evolve. Researches have yet to find why this happens, they just know it does.

Almost always, I recommend to new clients that they purchase a spiral notebook, not a pretty or attractive journal. In my experience, few people put the "real stuff" in actual journals, worrying they won't be perfect enough in what they write, will have to correct grammar or even that someone will find and read what they have written. For this reason, I suggest a basic notebook—something that will invite pure and raw emotion onto the paper. Writing on a computer does not offer the same benefit, mostly because we use different parts of our brain to type than to write and also because we constantly edit what we type as we go, not leaving room for the natural flow of emotion to emerge. Writing your emotions is intended to be a raw and imperfectly perfect expression of what you store inside.

I literally tell clients to write out their raw emotions, using whatever language and whatever tone they feel will convey what they have stored inside. I encourage them to give themselves permission to let loose—yell, scream, call situations or people names, naming what happened, how they felt, what they wish they could've said and what they would say if something similar happened again in the future. I urge them to write until they can't write any more, put the notebook away, and then take it out again as more layers or words emerge—which inevitably will. I tell clients to keep doing this until they find that they are repeating themselves and no new information is emerging. If they need to say the same things a few more times in different ways, then I encourage them to do so.

In the process of writing, I encourage people to pay attention to what they are learning about themselves in the process. Often, a person will see that their lack of assertion or action resulted in different outcomes in a situation. As will be discussed in the chapter about psychological health, you will learn that every emotion offers a cue to learn—it is an invitation to realign something that has become misaligned. For now, simply learn what you can and release what you must.

Once a person no longer finds something new to say, I instruct them to burn what they have written—not shred it because fragments are still left of their torn up words. There is something completely liberating about watching the energy of your written discomfort dissolve into the air. You receive relief, closure and freedom as the pages shrivel and turn to ash.

To save yourself some hassle, I usually tell people to line a fire pit, grill, large pan, clay pot or other heat-resistant container with aluminum foil so you can burn the pages within. Once the embers are cooled, you can simply wrap up the mess and toss it in the trash. For some, they prefer to disperse the ashes in a garden so the earth can absorb and transform the discomfort into something beautiful once again. The choice is yours. Either way is effective.

What I can guarantee is that you will feel better. You will be freed of the heaviness of some levels of the human condition and liberated from at least part of the darkness that once dimmed your view. You may also find solutions that have emerged as you release your words. You will clear your path so you can find brighter light at the end.

Many don't believe this exercise will assist in their healing until they have accomplished the task. But once they have, they repeat the exercise whenever necessary to peel away layers of the human condition that have piled up or blocked their view.

I encourage you to consider finding a safe place to keep your journal in the while of completing your process of release. Many avoid writing what they really feel and believe about the world and those around them for fear that someone will find and read their words. It is important to create the privacy and soulful space in which to release the darkness you have experienced. This vessel can be an integral part of your recovery process. There may be some appeal to releasing the pent-up feelings you've experienced during the pandemic and it might give you a head start on your path to healing.

CHAPTER THREE

THE MYTH AND MYSTERY OF SELF-CARE

The real trick of life is not to be in the know, but in the mystery

—Fred Alan Wolf

Several years ago, a primary care doctor came to see me as a client. She disclosed she had been experiencing low-grade, but persistent depression, general fatigue, significant stress from work and some ongoing health issues that were wearing her down. As always during an initial session, I asked what she did for self-care. It is an item I've listed on my intake forms since I opened my private practice in 2004. She looked at me a bit puzzled, and then said she wasn't quite sure. I coaxed out of her that she does enjoy long walks, healthy cooking and time spent reading, along with quality time with her husband and two children—when she has the time to do these things.

For the next few years, I helped her work on balancing her life, increasing leisure and fun, and setting better boundaries both at work and home. Like many overachieving caregivers, she often gave in to requests from others and got herself back where she started. Just before the pandemic, she confessed she had never heard the words "self-care" prior to that initial session several years ago. I was stunned, thinking all primary care providers must encourage their patients with these necessary actions. I interviewed her while writing this book and she said, "Honestly, I don't know how I would've handled the pandemic had I not already been seeing you to help with self-care. I might have even left my job." While self-care was once a mystery to this physician, it is no longer. It is a now a staple in her life—something that sustains and bolsters her especially in the toughest of times.

The revelation that this provider hadn't even heard the words "self-care" prior to her first session several years ago helped me understand the precarious imbalance many healthcare practitioners experience as they attempt to navigate their own human condition. It also helped me see a pressing need to get these words into our daily vocabulary, especially as we embark on the journey of rebuilding and restoring our lives post-COVID.

Early in the pandemic, I created a six-point list of things clients should keep in mind as they navigated the event. These are strategies I encourage when any significant event happens (elections, natural disasters, racial or other societal issues such as the Me Too movement or other disturbing events). They came in particularly handy with the rise of stress due to uncertainty of the pandemic: 1) identify three to five basic forms of self-care they could maintain regardless of conditions, 2) stay open to learning what they could about themselves, others and the world, for there was surely much to be understood by this historic event, 3) decide "who" they want to be as they navigate this challenging time, 4) do something spiritual or inspiring to keep them focused on their internal resources, 5) minimize the amount of news they watch and view only reputable forms of media, and 6) find ways to have some fun to buffer the heaviness and uncertainty of the situation. I reminded clients of these six suggestions often and many of them said it helped greatly in getting through the most difficult periods of isolation, fear and overwhelm. Interestingly, the hardest part of this list proved to be how to identify and maintain self-care activities, which seems to elude us all when life becomes misaligned.

Over time, I extended the conversations to help people understand the difference between self-care and "restorative actions" since people's stress deepened as the pandemic wore on. To me, self-care is performed mostly for coping and maintenance—something all of us surely need on a regular basis. These activities include the basics we are all taught from a young age: exercise, nutrition, rest and sleep, time with loved ones and leisure activities such as watching a movie or reading a book. All of these activities serve to buffer the frayed edges, but don't necessarily restore us from the inside out. They are meant to maintain our physical health, but not automatically sustain our inner light—our soul.

Particularly now, there is something deeper that needs to be restored and possibly even overhauled completely. Pre-COVID, many people's lives were already imbalanced, exhausting or unhappy due to the many possible stressors and circumstances already present. Our human condition is just that—a condition that often challenges our well-being, life satisfaction and general ability to cope. Once the pandemic hit, it added multiple heavy layers to what may have already been weighted down or misaligned. So, in fact, many of you were exhausted and stressed out prior to when the world decided to fall apart. Now that it is time to rebuild, you'll need the tools to do so.

To pull you out of the depths of a life-altering event, especially one that is ongoing and relentless such as a pandemic, requires more—it involves more intentional care to what we need to do to fill us up rather than just buff out what may have become rough or tattered. Many of you feel broken as a result of the work you have done to help others and it is time to take a deeper look at what will realign your own life, restore your inner light and help you heal from the difficulties you have faced. Essentially, not only will you, as healthcare workers, need to understand the necessity of self-care, you will also need to evolve beyond what you originally thought maintained your health and balance. This is the only way to truly find—and keep—your inner light.

When Self-Care Becomes A Burden

Greater love has no one than this,
than to lay down his life for his friends.
—John, 15:18

True story: I wrote this chapter while at the beach. I took my first week away from seeing clients since the beginning of the pandemic so I could do a bit of my own restoration while immersing myself in writing the beginning chapters of this book. Getting away is not only one of the things that I sorely missed most during the pandemic, but it is also one of the few things that allows me to clear my head, organize my thoughts and set a plan for moving forward in my own life. As I returned from the day's pre-writing walk on the beach, a silver medallion washed up right in front of me that had the above bible verse stamped on it.

Contrary to the above quote, the biggest challenge for most healthcare providers is their tendency to put others' lives so far in front of their own that they forget themselves altogether. It may seem cliché to hear that you really can't help others unless you help yourself. This is true, but it is also a double-edged myth. You can help others without serving yourself, but you will most certainly lose yourself along the way. It is also true that basic self-care is necessary, but insufficient in reclaiming your inner light.

Take, for instance, Mother Teresa, the Roman Catholic nun who was sainted for giving all she had to give and living her own life for the sake of the poor. What most people don't know is that she exhausted herself to the point of hospitalization several times in her life. Her dedication to helping others came at a significant but ongoing personal cost. Although she was praised for her unlimited dedication to serving others, she almost lost her own life many times as a result.

I'm a huge believer in the power of self-care. In fact, with the 2019 publication of my second book, *Recipe for Radiance: Mastering the Art and Soul of Self-Care*, I literally wrote the book on it! But in the midst of a global pandemic—especially as a healthcare provider—how do you maintain any semblance of care for self when you are so busy caring for others? The honest and realistic answer is, you probably do not.

The same physician I mentioned at the beginning of this chapter reported significantly more stress and exhaustion during the worst times of the pandemic for all of the same reasons you may have experienced. During one session at the end of 2020, she confessed that her self-care strategies had waned and said she felt like a "therapy client failure". We chuckled, but I also surprised her by saying that "Sometimes self-care becomes a burden." I then went on to tell her that lately I found myself foregoing many of my own typical tools that kept me afloat. I was just as depleted as the next healthcare provider and at the end of the day, I didn't have anything left in me to go for my routine walk, do my daily meditation, read like I'd always done before bed, talk to friends or even sit outside in nature—which was always my favorite restorative activity. Disclosing my own challenges with self-care at the time helped her see that during the worst of conditions, we tend to do the least to maintain our life-balance. It's just how it is and no self-imposed guilt will help you get back on track. You have to wait until you're ready.

No doubt, self-care became a burden for many during the pandemic. Many providers I interviewed admitted they were already notoriously bad at taking care of themselves prior to the virus's impact. One nurse laughed and said it is the "martyr part of us that gets in the way". Several providers who reported healthy pre-COVID routines admitted to giving up many of the basics that were once a steady part of their self-care diet. Others laughed and said they'd exchanged these healthy behaviors for eating and drinking more as well as binge-watching shows they would've never considered before the pandemic began. One front-line worker said she and her partner began keeping three different kinds of cookies in the house at all times, replenishing them every four or five days. Another practitioner who works for a drug and alcohol treatment center admitted to having a drink at the end of each day—something she felt guilty for given her work. A friend of mine—a social worker—also said she started drinking a gin and tonic each night after a long day of teletherapy.

The truth is, in order to benefit from self-care, you have to "fill up" with more than is seeping out. During the pandemic, very few healthcare providers were able to balance their lives enough to compensate for the demands that drained them. Moving forward, it will be important to learn about both the basics of self-care and the importance of restoring yourself at a deeper level so that when life throws challenges your way (which is almost always guaranteed in this human condition), you will be more prepared to overcome them.

Self-Care vs. Restoration

The work of restoration cannot begin until a problem is fully faced.
−Dan Allender

You can't restore something when you don't know what is broken or are unwilling to face it. The chapters describing Soul Health will help you assess the various "branches" or aspects of your life that might be imbalanced, broken or missing altogether. I've said throughout the pandemic that healthcare workers won't know what hit them until they have the time to assess. This book will help you to both consider which aspects of your life might need to be rebalanced or rebuilt and provide the stepping stones to create your path to healing. Just as each of your journeys has been different, your path to recovering from the pandemic will be as well.

While self-care, for many healthcare providers, is an oxymoron— words that seem to completely contradict one another—practitioners do seem to know that in order to heal beyond the body, much more needs to take place. You just might not know what "more" is.

In my book, *Recipe for Radiance*, I explain that to me, self-care *IS* soul care. In order to really restore ourselves, we must identify and engage in the activities that "feed" or nourish us deeply. While general self-care, such as exercise and good nutrition, are necessary to keep us physically healthy, overall vitality requires far more. As healthcare practitioners who want to recover fully from your experiences during the pandemic, you will need to take the time to assess what does and doesn't restore you at this deeper level. Also, as unique as each of us is, we all require our own personal combination of soul-care activities—our unique "recipe" that more fully fits our individual needs and more richly nourishes and balances our life.

Before exploring how to restore your life, it may be helpful to more objectively assess how much stress you have experienced during the span of the pandemic and what areas of life may have been the hardest hit. Keep in mind, many of you already experienced many stressful life events prior to COVID, so the impact of each may have compounded your ability to cope overall.

The American Stress Institute has long studied the direct impact that particular life stressors have on the likelihood of physical illness (including stress, depression, and anxiety). The Holmes-Rahe Social Readjustment Scale is the best-known assessment for vulnerability to illness as related to life stressors. Keep in mind, this scale was created decades before the pandemic and has been updated along the way. Although many of the items on this list may apply, you may have to "create your own" categories to fully appreciate the amount of stress you experienced throughout this challenging time.

Take a few minutes to complete the inventory below by adding up the Life Change Units (LCU) associated with the stressors you have experienced in the last year. (I would suggest including all events you experienced throughout and following the pandemic that you consider stressful to more accurately access the ongoing impact.) If a certain item has occurred more than once, multiply the LCU by the number of times it has occurred and then add it to your total. (For example, if you have moved residences more than once, you will add 20 LCU to the total for each time you have moved.) You may also add your own categories particular to your experience and estimate the applicable LCU in keeping with the list. Completion of this scale is simply meant to give you a basic understanding of what you have withstood during the pandemic.

HOLMES-RAHE SOCIAL READJUSTMENT SCALE

Rank	Life event	Life Change Unit
1.	Death of spouse	100
2.	Divorce	73
3.	Separation from mate or spouse	73
4.	Death of a close family member	63
5.	Detention in jail or other institution	63
6.	Major personal injury or illness	53
7.	Marriage	50
8.	Being fired/let go from work	47
9.	Reconciliation with mate or spouse	45
10.	Retirement	45
11.	Major change in health or behavior of a family member	44
12.	Pregnancy	40
13.	Sexual difficulties	39
14.	Gaining of new family member (birth, adoption, older adult)	39
15.	Major business readjustment	39
16.	Major change in financial state	38
17.	Death of close friend	37
18.	Changing to different line of work	36
19.	Change in number of arguments with spouse	35
20.	Taking on a mortgage (new home/business)	31
21.	Foreclosure of mortgage or loan	30
22.	Major changes in responsibilities at work	29
23.	Son or daughter leaving home	29
24.	Trouble with in-laws	29
25.	Outstanding personal achievement	28
26.	Spouse beginning or ceasing work outside the home	26
27.	Beginning or ceasing formal schooling	26

Rank	Life event	Life Change Unit
28.	Major change in living conditions (new home, remodeling, etc.)	25
29.	Revision of personal habits (health/personal development)	24
30.	Trouble with boss	23
31.	Major changes in work hours or conditions	20
32.	Change in residence	20
33.	Changing to a new school	20
34.	Major change in type or amount of recreation	19
35.	Major change in church activities	19
36.	Major change in social activities	18
37.	Mortgage or loan (new car, home improvement)	17
38.	Major change in sleeping habits	16
39.	Major change in number of family get-togethers	15
40.	Major change in eating habits	15
41.	Vacation	13
42.	Major holidays	12
43.	Minor violations of the law	11

Your total number of LCU: _____

Your susceptibility to illness related to the number of stressors experienced can be assessed as follows:

Less than 150: Significantly reduced chance of getting sick in the next year

150 to 199: Suggests mild life crisis or slightly increased chance of becoming ill in the next year

200 to 299: Suggests moderate life crisis and moderately increased chance of getting sick in the next year

Over 300: Suggests a major life crisis with greatly increased chances of getting sick in next year.

Some of the items on the list might seem surprising. For example, most people think holidays are full of fun and joy. However, since many didn't get to enjoy holidays during the pandemic, it may have seemed more stressful than joyful. A lack of vacations can be stressful for some people for many reasons, including myself, as I rely on time away to refresh my perspective. All these life events, as well as the ones you may have added, can make your radiance dwindle. It is what you do to recharge and restore yourself that makes the difference.

While all of us experience stress as part of our typical human condition, the pandemic has added multiple heavy layers. Basic self-care practices can have a positive effect in buffering strain when you experience intense stressors. They also serve as preventative measures for maintaining health during tumultuous times. Certain aspects of your habits, lifestyle, and environment can make you more or less vulnerable to the negative effects of stress.

Researchers Miller and Smith offered a self-assessment that illustrates the positive impact of engaging in frequent self-care activities to prevent physical illness. Essentially, you can effectively counterbalance the negative impact of stressful circumstances with the positive impact of intentional behaviors that you have specifically identified as activities that preserve and enhance self- and soul-care. If your level of positive impact from self-care activities exceeds the negative impact of stressors, then you not only maintain a manageable or even healthy level of health and radiance, but you also neutralize future detrimental effects.

Take some time to complete the survey below to determine your vulnerability to illness according to the stress you currently experience.

VULNERABILITY TO STRESS SCALE

Score each item from 1 (almost always) to 5 (never) as it applies to you
.

_____1. I eat at least one hot, nutritious meal a day.

_____2. I get seven to eight hours of sleep at least four nights a week.

_____3. I am affectionate with others regularly.

_____4. I have at least one relative who lives within 50 miles on whom I can rely.

_____5. I exercise to the point of sweating at least twice a week.

_____6. I smoke fewer than ten cigarettes a day. (Score 0 if you don't smoke.)

_____7. I drink fewer than five alcoholic drinks a week. (Score 0 if you don't drink alcohol.)

_____8. I am about the proper weight for my height and age.

_____9. I have enough money to meet basic expenses and needs.

_____10. I feel strengthened by my religious (or spiritual) beliefs.

_____11. I attend club or social activities on a regular basis.

_____12. I have several close friends and acquaintances.

_____13. I have one or more friends to confide in about personal matters.

_____14. I am basically in good health.

_____15. I am able to speak openly about my feelings when angry or worried.

_____16. I discuss problems about chores, money, and daily living with people I live with.

_____17. I do something just for fun at least once a week.

_____18. I am able to organize my time and don't feel pressured.

_____19. I drink fewer than three cups of coffee (tea or soda) a day.

_____20. I allow myself quiet time at least once during each day.

_____**Your total number of points**

Less than 50 points: You are not particularly vulnerable to stress.
50-80 points: Moderate vulnerability to stress.
Over 80 points: High vulnerability to stress.

As you can see, the amount of balance you maintain is directly associated with the type and frequency of activities you include in your ongoing self- and soul-care plan. At one extremely stressful point in graduate school, I took the Holmes-Rahe scale to estimate the amount of stress I was under compared to the amount of self-care I was doing to balance my life at the time. My score was over 550 points—a level that would predict a major negative impact on my overall health. However, because I had already identified and participated in several self-care activities on a regular basis, my risk of becoming ill (according to the Vulnerability to Stress Scale) was minimal (a score of 38 on the survey above). This example illustrates that taking a proactive approach to wellness is the key to leading a satisfying and balanced life.

Without assessing each of you, I can assume that your scores on both the Holmes-Rahe scale and the Vulnerability to Stress scale are rather high, but you shouldn't be alarmed. These are just measures that help educate you for the future to the importance of keeping a balance between self-sustaining activities when in the midst of stress and chaos. These assessments can also help to illuminate some initial areas of your life needing improvement.

After completing these assessments, there is likely little doubt that your ability to restore your life post-COVID is related to the relationship between the amount of energy you expend because of your everyday stress and the amount of energy you replace by engaging in your self- and soul-care activities. During my interviews, I found it interesting to hear how different professionals perceived their ability to cope, especially when their spouses thought otherwise. One physician sounded rather upbeat and positive in his responses, but his wife revealed that he would return home after a long day to stare at a wall. She said she couldn't speak with him in the evening because there was very little left of him to share.

Another spouse I interviewed said that she and her husband—also a physician—had contracted COVID about 10 months into the pandemic. While she recovered fairly quickly, other than a loss of taste and smell that lingered, he suffered from severe complications, was hospitalized several times and almost died. Once released, he threw himself back into work in order to cope. She went on to work on self-care and changing things in her life that were already undesirable, while he returned to his previously driven ways. Both used their respective methods as a form of coping, but only one heeded a wake-up call and improved her life.

In the interviews I conducted, females admitted the most emotional distress, while males confessed using alcohol and sex (frequent activity with a partner or spouse, pornography or even affairs) to decrease their stress. More females reported accessing mental health care, which is commonly the case. In fact, women tend to tend to seek assistance more than their male counterparts including through reading, purchasing over ninety percent of personal development books.

Typically, most education about self-care focuses on the following:

1. Self-Care in daily routine:
   + Sensible nutrition
   + Adequate sleep and rest
   + Regular exercise
   + Awareness of stress level
   + Acknowledgement of reactions to stressful circumstance

2. Self-Care at work:
   + Diversifying tasks and varying caseload
   + Taking breaks
   + Taking vacation days
   + Using relaxation techniques
   + Seeking support of colleagues
   + Establishing a professional support network
   + Recognizing limitations

3. Self-Care outside of the workplace
   + Spending time with family and friends
   + Staying connected through community events, religious groups, etc.
   + Engaging in pleasurable activities unrelated to work

+ Exercising mindfulness about one's own thoughts and feelings
+ Engaging in rejuvenating activities such as meditation, prayer or relaxation
+ Seeking professional assistance when necessary

Although all of these suggestions sound well and good in normal times, they are exactly the kinds of recommendations healthcare providers reported as frustrating after receiving them from employers during the pandemic. Those I interviewed saw these as nice reminders, but couldn't see how to implement them while in the throes of their tumultuous times. Some were able to maintain a few, but most felt more offended, inadequate and frustrated than cared for and supported when the reminders were presented.

Readiness, resources and time to change a lifestyle are all necessary in actually restoring your life and setting your path to healing. The next few chapters will help you assess whether you are ready to embark on your healing journey. Throughout my almost thirty-four years of providing mental health care and wellness services, I've come to appreciate, both for myself and those I serve, that there comes a time and place for everything. Until a person is ready to start on a path, there is no movement forward. Unfortunately, sometimes it takes hitting rock bottom in order to rise at all. This will be the case for many as you attempt to recover from your experiences during the pandemic. When you are ready, the path will be waiting.

CHAPTER FOUR
THE THREE QUESTIONS OF DISCERNMENT FOR LIVING A RADIANT LIFE

Let discernment be your trustee, and mistakes your teacher.
—T.F. HODGE

Later, you will learn more about the *Soul Health Model*, the blueprint to restoring your life and evolving beyond your experiences during the pandemic. This roadmap will provide the steps to help you "clean out" what no longer serves you, while "filling up" with what does. But many have a hard time deciding what key aspects of life need adjustment and few know how to put it into practice. Since the second edition of my book, *Soul Health: Aligning with Spirit for Radiant Living*, was published, I tightened the process of helping people assess and redesign their lives with "The Three Questions of Discernment for Living a Radiant Life". In the next chapter, you will learn the procedure or protocol, by which you will be able to slowly, but consciously and intentionally shift your life in a better direction. Both have already assisted many in turning their lives "right-side up", simply by changing the way they think about life and how they decide what is important.

Because restoring your life beyond basic self-care requires a bit of deeper thinking, I created a simple, three-step system of inquiry that will more fully assess your needs to more directly create your personalized path to healing. I've seen tremendous progress and shifts in both perspective and practice when people apply this system to their lives. I have used it, myself, for years and have found my life steadily improving regardless of the challenges that were placed in my path. Clients used it throughout the pandemic and our conversations reminded me at times that I needed to put these questions back into action for myself.

The Three Questions of Discernment for Radiant Living

Following are the three queries everyone should make when deciding how to lead a more restored, fulfilling and soulful life. Beyond the necessity of basic self-care, these questions will assist you in doing both the real assessment and healing practices that are necessary to transcend the circumstances you experienced as a healthcare worker during the pandemic.

Ask yourself:

1. Is it meaningful?

2. Is it necessary?

3. Does it feed my soul?

Immediately, you are likely to experience a shift in understanding how you've led your life up to this point. Even if you ponder these questions without reading on, something will change. You will go down a path of assessing your life more deeply, leading you to a much more fulfilled and balanced life.

Let's explore these questions individually.

Is it meaningful? What does "meaningful" really mean? Webster's dictionary defines it as "having a serious, important, or useful quality or purpose". While we may think things are meaningful, once you apply this definition to the elements of your life, you may decide to choose differently. Also, what was once meaningful may have changed. This is part of evolution. It is important to periodically assess the quality or purpose of the things, people and activities with which we choose to engage, in case something has shifted or changed.

Once the fog from your experience with COVID-19 clears, you may find yourself assessing everything differently. A life-altering experience such as a pandemic, no doubt, changes what we once believed was important. For many, the experience solidified the field of healthcare as the right choice for them, while some may decide to leave the field altogether. As you will learn through reading about the *Soul Health Model*, it is essential to determine what does or doesn't fit into the "branches" of your own, unique tree of life in order to really align yourself for optimal living. If the "it" still fits that branch, then you will choose to maintain. If "it" doesn't feel meaningful any more, you may choose to let go and grow beyond. That is the process of discernment that will take place as you evaluate how to restore your life.

Is it necessary? The dictionary says that which is necessary is "something to be done or achieved" or "something that is present, needed and essential". For the sake of the soul, this question is tricky. Our human condition and ego—the part of our being that mediates between consciousness and the unconscious—often denies what our inner self requires for maintaining our personal identity. For instance, we may think we need to do a million things to be a good person, partner or employee while our soul is screaming to balance our lives and slow down. In this case, our need for importance overrides the necessities of our soul and we end up tired, frustrated, resentful and sick once more. Our ego tends to exaggerate what we think we need, wanting "more" of something, when in fact, we might need much less. This applies to love, work, social interactions, sex, material objects and so on. However, if you apply whether something is meaningful and feeds your soul to the question of "Is it necessary?" it helps to answer the question in a much clearer way.

As a healthcare worker who is dedicated and even driven to "help", this question can be particularly challenging to answer. You are likely inclined to answer what is "necessary" for the sake of the other people in your life rather than for yourself. In the case of the physician mentioned early in this chapter, this question was the one that often stumped her. She automatically switched back into "helper", "mom" or "wife" mode, even to her own detriment. Much of our time spent working together was focused on helping her find the balance between helping herself and assisting others.

I get it. Your identity as a health provider is tied to your willingness to help. But when you are in need of a restorative practice to get you back into the "light" of your own life, you will likely have to adjust this as well.

Does it feed your soul? Does the "it" nourish you in such a way that it brightens your inner light rather than drains or dampens it? Does the thing, person or activity fill you up and sustain you even through the most stressful times? Do you feel sustained and supported when other parts of life are getting you down? Does that which feeds your soul keep you afloat even when you feel you are getting submerged?

Let me use a personal example of something that sustained me at least for a while at the beginning of the pandemic. Travel is one of the things that feeds my soul very deeply and I make it a priority to keep me well nourished. My trips to Bhutan, Nepal and the Galapagos Islands in November and December of 2019 fed me for quite a while. For me, these were all spiritually-based adventures and I was deeply sustained by my experience in each country in different, but related ways. When travel halted in early 2020, I didn't really feel deprived or depleted in that way until the spring of 2021 when my "travel tank" started to feel rather low. Between March of 2020 and April of 2021, the only place I visited occasionally was Charlotte, North Carolina where my best friend serendipitously moved a couple of years before the pandemic began. Her move from 1700 miles away prior to the arrival of the virus served as a godsend, so we could occasionally use each other's homes as safe pandemic getaways.

My daily walks in nature, silent time to myself, playing with my dogs, spiritual reading and practices, fun with friends and many other activities all satiate my inner ally. Luckily, many of them continued during the pandemic. I intentionally create space for these activities on a daily basis, knowing that the drain I feel during the week will always be restored if I make certain to engage in the things that fill me up.

Exploring what is meaningful and necessary as well as learning what feeds your soul takes both consciousness and intentional inquiry, which is why I call these questions *The Three Questions of Discernment for Radiant Living*. Without conscious awareness and examination of what nourishes you deeply, you will likely not lead a life that offers constant and consistent fulfillment. You will not be guaranteed a restored life or overall Soul Health.

Although I repeatedly use these questions with clients, I didn't know how helpful they would be in talking with those I interviewed. One of the last interchanges I had with the physician leader I mentioned at the end of Chapter One helped me see how these questions of discernment changed his outlook. He mentioned how they helped him reframe his life as well as set him on a path to shift what he saw as broken. He said, "The third criteria, feed my soul, has changed everything, including what is meaningful and what is important. It has become the driving factor." He added that previously the soul wouldn't have had much meaning for him until he embarked on his own spiritual journey a handful of years prior to when COVID hit the United States. Between feeling "cracked open" by the events and professional responsibilities of the pandemic and his readiness to go within, these questions resonated and allowed him to set out on his own path to healing.

After considering these questions of discernment, think about the following:

- What would be different if you led your life using these three inquiries?
- What would you eliminate from your life?

- ✦ What would you add to your life?
- ✦ Would feeding your soul help to eliminate unhealthy and less "nourishing" behaviors?
- ✦ What would be different about *you* overall if your soul was well fed?

I have long lived life saying I wanted to minimize regret. These questions allow me to do this and help me to clean out and adjust my "tree of life" (my personal tree of soul health) so that I can shed what no longer serves me, while filling myself up with only things that enhance my inner light. As I continually work to align my own tree for radiant living, I can then serve as an example to others to do the same.

Although examining the different "branches" of your overall health will take some time, these questions of discernment will serve as a quick guide to assess whether something is useful or possibly even harmful in your life. Along with aligning your branches, these questions will allow you to deepen your awareness about what will lead you down your path to restoring your life.

Readiness to Change and Heal

Progress is impossible without change; and those who cannot change their minds cannot change anything.
—George Bernard Shaw

Change is not easy, especially when you're exhausted from something like a global health event. While many models of behavior change exist, it is important to realize that *readiness* to change makes all the difference.

Researchers and authors, Prochaska and DiClemente, recognized in the early 70's that individuals go through many stages while changing something in their lives. They created an integrative model to conceptualize the process of intentional behavior change, which can be applied to all theoretical models, behaviors and settings. Their Transtheoretical Model consists of six stages: Pre-Contemplative, Contemplative, Preparation, Action, Maintenance and Relapse. When I was a professor, I taught this model to residents and medical, nursing and physician assistant students, as well as to clients enrolled in a comprehensive weight management program. For weight management patients, I would ask, "How ready are you to lose weight?" They would all enthusiastically respond with something like "very ready!" But when I asked them how ready they were to do what it took to lose the weight, most quickly backpedaled.

The reality is that change is hard and it takes time. We can't just go through the motions and assume we will get to where we'd like to be as fast as we'd like. Assessing where you are in your own readiness to get to a brighter path and future will help you determine which are the most reasonable and realistic first steps.

Pre-Contemplative—This stage is the early process of change when a person might not have even considered the need to do something differently. The person might be resistant or unwilling to take suggestions or steps to improve their situation. They may be willing to focus on other things they see as more important, even if these things add to their challenging situation. Remember, people don't usually change unless they are tired of themselves or their situations. Therefore, someone in the Pre-Contemplative stage is not usually even thinking about things being different. *Main tasks*: Look for opportunities to learn, assess and admit that change could produce a better outcome than what you currently experience.

Contemplation—During this stage, a person has more awareness of the problem, but might remain ambivalent about taking steps toward change. They might rationalize or minimize their situation, with fluctuating levels of interest in altering their behavior. Either way, they are more aware that they are uncomfortable even if they aren't ready to take action to improve their circumstances. *Main tasks*: Explore reasons to change, including the pros and cons, as well as beginning the assessment process for what would be most easy to change.

Preparation—In this phase, the individual is ready for change and sees the need to prepare to actually move forward. A person readily admits the need for change, accepting that if they don't, worse consequences will likely arise. They start looking for alternatives and often reach out for help at this time. *Main tasks*: Educate yourself for options available, talk to professionals who can help, start to develop a realistic plan for change.

Action—The person begins to engage in actions to turn their life "right-side up". They start to create a plan, make changes and use professional help or resources to assist them in moving forward. *Main tasks*: Explore and implement small, realistic changes or tasks that are likely to be successful. Identify potential roadblocks and "hazards" that might impede progress. Find healthy rewards to reinforce commitment to change.

Maintenance—This stage marks the time when the individual has made changes and is looking for methods to sustain what they have altered. They focus less on refraining from old behaviors and turn their focus to more of a "recovery" lifestyle. Many behaviors have become habits and are much easier to consider as part of their lives. *Main tasks*: Affirm self for positive changes while remaining realistic that old behaviors might persist. Make a plan for getting off track and how to redirect focus back to positive change. Review warning signs for potential relapse.

Relapse—The person might have a slip or return to obstructive behavior. During this stage, individuals may repeat behaviors they are trying to change, might engage in different but equally problematic behavior, or feel shame for having turned back to old ways. *Main tasks*: Explore how and why "slips" occurred, while looking for methods to avoid them again in the future. Review your plan for change and adjust as needed to provide more successful and realistic outcomes.

It is normal—and even part of the learning process—to return to previous behaviors after you've decided to change something in your life. If change were easy, life would be a breeze. I offer you this model to help you realize that your healing process will take time and patience to achieve. Many clients have asked over the years if I get tired of digging them out of their old repeated patterns. Because I know the cycles of change are part of the process—part of evolution, I expect that even you—healthcare providers will falter on your healing path at times. It's a given part of the process.

So, when it comes to learning self-care and more deeply restorative strategies, healthcare providers could use some patience and understanding along the way. You will also need a blueprint as well as procedures and protocols of your own to get you beyond where you are today. The next chapter will provide a different kind of procedure to follow to assist in your own change process.

CHAPTER FIVE
THE PROCEDURE OF A LIFETIME

You can act to change and control your life;
and the procedure, the process is its own reward.
—AMELIA EARHART

While examining the branches of the *Soul Health Model* will help you to realign your life within each area, you still need a "procedure" or "protocol" to help you decide what to adjust, one way or another. As you read earlier, it is not enough for me to help someone heal; instead I want to help them *evolve*. If you think about it—and if you remember the statistics—most healthcare workers were burned out and stressed prior to the pandemic, If this is true, why would I want to return you to that already depleted and misaligned state?

My mission is to help you slowly, but consciously and intentionally change the elements of your life so, in the long run, it always feels bright, satisfied and fulfilled. This might seem like a fantasy or pipe dream, but I have hundreds of former clients and workshop participants—and possibly more than a few of those I interviewed for this book—who can attest to this. It was both affirming and fun to offer what I knew worked for others to those I interviewed since many seemed ready to be guided to a brighter and more fortified path. My hope now is that you will find the same excitement in restoring your life as well.

The information I offer below is new. I created the acronym to the word "Evolve" in the fall of 2020, hoping to offer a conscious path to those who want to grow beyond their old circumstances. Little did I know that it would come in handy in writing this book. As I realized that healthcare providers have a procedure for everything but themselves, it made sense to use this to help you evaluate what needs to be restored, as well as how to take the steps to do it. This "procedure" can be applied to the examination of your branches of health to build a strong and vibrant "tree of life", as well as to enhance the entire tree. Just as trees somehow know how to overcome adverse conditions, you can use this information to heal beyond your own.

E.V.O.L.V.E.

Below is a procedure or protocol you can follow to both help you heal from the many layers of the human condition that overwhelmed and possibly wounded you and advance beyond this state to create a much more balanced and radiant life. Each step will be discussed further to more fully explain how to use this process of realigning your life on your healing path.

E—**Examine**—explore the factors causing disruption or blocking your path
V—**Vision**—imagine a bright and renewed future ahead
O—**Observe**—notice and perceive what is significant
L—**Learn**—grasp the information and details that will help you grow
V—**Venture**—do something outside your norm to get somewhere new
E—**Elevate**—lift yourself to higher and more radiant (brighter) ground

Examine

As a healthcare provider, you examine your patients or assess what is amiss so you can treat them and help them feel better. The same is true for you as you find your way on your own healing path. In the following chapters, you will be encouraged to "assess" each branch of health that pertains to the layers of the human condition that were likely affected or negatively impacted throughout both your personal and professional roles during the pandemic. There are many challenging and even horrific things we experience in life, but perhaps the most difficult task is to turn the focus to you—to look at what in your own life needs to be healed to feel more balanced. I've heard many healthcare providers say during therapy that it is much easier to address issues that are apparent in someone else, but in order to properly heal from this terrible event you must examine your own life as well.

Socrates said, "The unexamined life is not worth living." I would add that it would be empty, unevolved and even "stuck" if we didn't explore the elements of our lives that block our growth. Although you might feel stuck or blocked in moving forward from the events of the pandemic, once you remove these blocks, your evolution and life satisfaction will remain in a more vibrant and forward-moving state. Once you examine and take steps to improve your life, future obstruction will be far less likely.

Vision

Karma Brown (yes, that's her real name) said, "You have a right to change your present if it doesn't fit with the future you envision." No one I know would say they have a perfect life, especially following a life-altering world event. However, we all tend to long and hope for something better, regardless of how good or bad we might judge our lives to be. That is what keeps us going. As you read more about the "soul" part of health—you will come to understand that the driving force within you is also your guiding force in creating a more appealing and fulfilling life. As you imagine a bright and renewed future ahead when you realign the branches of your human condition, you will have a better idea of what you do or don't need on your healing path. Keep in mind, that when we are in a dark night of the soul—the time when everything looks dim and bleak—we often struggle to see a brighter future. But as you work to improve even one branch on your tree of life, you will notice how this positively impacts other branches as well. The clarity you receive in the process will provide the motivation and inspiration to continue moving forward.

Remember, the light within you that created the dedication to do the work you did as a healthcare provider during the pandemic is also the light that will help you envision life beyond this difficult time. You just need to give yourself permission to create, accept and receive a better life for yourself.

Observe

Your path to healing is all about noticing and perceiving what needs to change. The beginning of your restoration process will likely entail getting the basics of your life back in order—returning to some semblance of a post-COVID "normal" in terms of day-to-day routine, structure and balance. To really enhance your life in the long run, you will need to observe what is and isn't working, as well as make note of any resistance in creating a better path. This is what the *Soul Health Model* is all about—it provides the blueprint to help you observe and notice the parts of your life that need to be cleaned out or adjusted, while determining what needs to be added or "nourished" to sustain you in a different and more positive way moving forward. Your willingness to note what needs some work will help to deeply fortify you for the rest of your life.

This is where *The Three Questions of Discernment for Living a Radiant Life* come in (i.e. what is meaningful, necessary and feeds your soul). As you observe what you need and don't need in each of your branches of health, you can apply these questions to be more discerning of what each branch requires on your unique path to healing.

American teacher and philosopher, Amos Bronson Allcott said, "Observation, more than books and experience, more than persons, is the prime educator." Until we can consciously observe who we are, what we need and how to move forward, we only go through the motions. After speaking with over one hundred healthcare providers for this book, I believe many of you are tired of doing the same old thing, which makes you more ready to recover and step onto your path to a better future.

Learn

Your personal evolution requires you to learn about yourself along the way. As an encouragement to my clients early on in the pandemic, I nudged openness to learning whatever they were supposed to learn about themselves, others and the world during this difficult time. When we feel we are getting something out of a situation no matter how challenging the situation might be, we always feel better. But how does one stay open to learning when everything they once knew to be true is suddenly different? Fortunately, there's likely something to be learned from unexpected uncertainty as well.

One of the biggest lessons during the pandemic has been to accept others' opinions, values and beliefs. This has been a constant challenge for many as differences about mask wearing, social distancing and vaccines emerged. As you will see later in the book, the interpersonal relationships we hold often create the most significant opportunities to learn about ourselves and others.

"There are certain life lessons that you can only learn in the struggle." Author, Idowu Koyenikan made this statement, acknowledging the power of learning through life's challenges. When we stay open to learning through even our most difficult or dark times, it always feels more acceptable, palatable and even welcome to experience these events. We often learn in retrospect, instead of right in the moment anyway. So, it is very likely that your healing process will offer you much growth just in learning about who you were prior to the pandemic, who you became as a result and who you want to be moving forward. Grasping and embracing what you have learned will, no doubt, help you grow. Both your evolution and true healing depends on it.

Venture

During my interviews with healthcare practitioners, some said they wished they could make a run for it, leave everything behind and just start a new life. Although these might have been escapist fantasies for some, I'm guessing a few will do just that once they feel the time is right.

Your healing path will ask you to do much that you would've never done prior to the arrival of COVID-19, both personally and professionally. I heard many say they didn't want to necessarily leave healthcare, but they wanted to do something different once they had the chance. I heard others say they wanted to move to a different community, part of the country or even abroad. About a third said they would change something about their relationships, whether to work on marriages, leave them or create a whole new circle of friends. Many said they had taken up hobbies and wanted to integrate even more when their schedules allowed. A colleague said she just wanted to have more fun in general, including dancing more often as well as engaging in other active, but entertaining leisure time endeavors.

Venturing onto a new and higher path will require you to do something outside your norm. While many prior to the pandemic thought "this is all there is", some now realize they want—and even deserve— something more. Your willingness to venture onto higher ground and into a brighter future will take doing something different—and possibly unexpected—to get you there.

Philosopher and rhetorician, Lucius Annaeus Seneca said, "It's not because things are difficult that we dare not venture. It's because we dare not venture that they are difficult." He meant that when we don't venture into something new, our lives are more difficult than if we had. The research on regret supports this, since most people regret what they didn't do more than what they did.

Elevate

During interviews, I heard statements like, "This brought me to my knees", "I've sunk lower than ever before" and "I'm so buried under that I don't know how to get back up". Eventually, you will be ready to lift yourself to higher and more radiant ground. Like those you helped out of the depths of COVID-19, your own path to healing will lead you to an elevated place where you can see life from a greater and more enjoyable viewpoint. The hike there might seem daunting, but the summit is always worth the climb.

I have helped hundreds of client's back to the "top". I've found that the more they learn and grow, the more they want to continue learning and growing. Once they reach a point they didn't think they could reach, they want to go even higher. There's something inspiring and motivating about growth once on the path; once on it, you really don't want to stop reaching for the next summit.

Many of you will look back at the time you spent during the pandemic and realize you made it to a place you never thought you could manage. You will realize something got you there and also got you through. Statistically, it is likely that you will never have to push yourself to the top again, like you did during this harrowing time—something much worse than literally climbing the world's highest mountain. The reflection about your experiences will change you. The experiences already *have*. But now it's time to get you to the top of your healing journey as well. Elevating yourself out of the darkness and rising above the challenges is not only possible, it is your right. You just need the tools and "gear" to get you there.

The E.V.O.L.V.E. "procedure" is unlike any you have learned so far. It is not necessarily a "step-by-step" process and it isn't clinical in nature, but neither is your healing path. In my experience over the last thirty-four years of working in mental health, I've found that personal development and evolution aren't linear any more than the path people took when they fell down, especially when you really want to overcome something tragic or something that affected you at the core of who you are. The process is slower than most want it to be, but this pace is necessary to really get to the bottom of what needs to change to take a person to their higher ground.

By *examining* what needs to be adjusted, *envisioning* how things could be better, *observing* what is and isn't working in your life, *learning* what you can about your process, *venturing* into new territory and *elevating* yourself to a new and brighter level, you will be well on your way on your healing path.

The Path of Personal Evolution

One can choose to go back toward safety or forward
toward growth. Growth must be chosen again and again;
fear must be overcome again and again.
–Abraham Maslow

There are two stories I like to share with clients to get them on their path to healing. One pertains to a conversation I had with a client years ago about his frustrations with his own healing process and the other was an observation I made during my later years of graduate school. Both have served to remind me that sometimes healing may seem to move more slowly and less smoothly than we would like, but once on the path, it is in constant motion, nonetheless.

"The First Fish that Flopped Onto Land"

About ten years ago, a chemist came to see me to help him deal with family issues and also some generalized anxiety. He worked for a pharmaceuticals manufacturer, designing and testing potential new releases. His concerns about his family of origin were fairly typical—difficulty breaking away from parents who wanted to be overinvolved. His anxiety was both genetically- and situationally-based, with ongoing stress from work forming the latter. As usual, I encouraged natural management through exercise, caffeine reduction, relaxation, cognitive strategies and other methods, then eventually suggested he try a low-dose anxiolytic to help with a genetic pre-disposition to anxiety. After a few months, he found himself feeling markedly better and we set on the path to dealing more with the family issues that had been present for years. About six months into his treatment, he plopped himself on my couch and asked "When will I ever feel better and get past all of this?" He noted that his stress had returned at a high level and he perceived himself to be heading back to square one.

I listened carefully for about twenty minutes as he unloaded and told me why he thought he had fully regressed. Then I said, "Think about how long it took for the first fish to flop onto land. After millions of years, he finally got tired of swimming in his own muck and decided to stay on land. He was finally ready to change." Being a scientist, my client thought about what I meant and relaxed, knowing that he might appear to go backwards, but he knew he would then move forward again, out of his "muck" when he was ready to move to higher ground. He understood that once he learned enough about his process—to not repeat old patterns or get stuck in old thoughts—he would evolve beyond the things he wanted to leave behind.

Moral of the story: healing is not a linear or "clean" process. You will likely circle back to some old ways of living, behaving, feeling and thinking before you permanently move beyond them. It's just part of the process. It is also a definite part of evolution.

"Shifting Sands"

The second anecdotal story has served me well, even in writing this book. I attended graduate school in Indiana, just a couple hours away from Lake Michigan. To get away from school, I liked to visit the Indiana Dunes National Seashore—now designated a national park. Just a short drive from Chicago, this natural landmark spans fifteen miles along the southern shore of the lake. At the end of my third year in the program, my best friend visited and we took a drive up to the dunes. While she was walking down the shore, I stood knee-deep in the water looking out as far as the eye can see. The expanse of the lake makes you think you are looking at an ocean, sailboats and waves included in the view.

As I stood there observing everyone looking out to sea, something made me turn around. As I glanced at the dunes, I realized that they were in constant, gentle motion. A light breeze passed over the dunes toward the lake, causing cascading sheets of sand to make their way to the bottom. I'd look back up to the top to see several more sheets caress, cover and descend the landscape, quietly, but constantly changing how it appeared. I stood and watched the movement for quite some time, recognizing that while everyone faced the lake looking for the "big" event—whatever that might be—the real show was taking place behind them. The constant, reliable and consistent experience—the continual change—was happening right there all the time.

The awareness I had while watching the dunes change before me was profound. I realized that what seemed like a static process taking a long time to change was actually a constant motion. Although slow and almost unrecognizable, evolution occurs right in front of us—we just have to notice it.

Your path to healing won't go as fast as you would like, it won't appear constant or consistent and it won't happen in a "straight line". But if you commit to the process of building your path and remain dedicated to your healing as much as you have been for the healing of others, you will reach your new summit—you will reach and stay on higher ground.

The decision to heal is a tough one, but it won't be nearly as hard as what you've already experienced. You may not know what is on the other side once your life is healed, but moving beyond your struggles will provide you with the wisdom to reach a level of really *living*. Healing from the emotional and physical discomfort you experienced during the pandemic is part of the process. But it is the time at which you advance beyond your discomfort that will bring the most complete relief, as well as the most enriched meaning to your life. Your personal investment in *you* is essential.

As you explore the *Soul Health Model* to balance your personal branches of health, keep in mind *The Three Questions of Discernment* and the *E.V.O.L.V.E.* method of taking you forward. Both will facilitate a deeper level of understanding as you reach a higher and brighter level of radiant health. In Part Three of this book, you will learn how to put it all together to create your personalized plan—your healing path. But for now, explore the model and the branches of health so you'll know what to prioritize first.

Your healing path will lead you to a better life—perhaps one you never thought was possible. That's part of personal evolution.

PART TWO
THE LIGHT BEYOND

Even the darkest night will end and the sun will rise.
—Victor Hugo

CHAPTER SIX
THE SOUL HEALTH MODEL
Healing Below the Surface

The root is certainly a more decisive factor than
what is growing above ground. After all, it is the
root that looks after the survival of the organism.

–Peter Wohlleben

The pandemic has affected all of us at a deep and complicated level.
It has penetrated all aspects of our human condition, which may
have already been challenged prior to the arrival of COVID-19. Now,
the question is how do we rebalance our lives when so much has shifted,
changed and left us wilted and/or broken?

It will likely take a deeper understanding and method of healing to
help you get past your experience. Just as no lab test can tell you what
is now amiss, no procedure you've learned thus far will help you heal.
But that's about to change.

Early in my training as a psychologist, I came across the National
Wellness Institute's (NWI) model of "wellness." The model included six
components of health—physical, psychological, social, environmental,
intellectual, and spiritual—which, when balanced, were assumed to assist
a person in reaching their fullest potential or their highest achieved sense

of feeling "well." This model was not included as part of my formal education, but I immediately started to conceptualize my clinical work from this perspective. Like most, I was taught the classic "bio-psycho-social" model, but the NWI model allowed me to expand my understanding of what was and wasn't working in my clients' lives—not to mention my own. It just made more sense than the methods I'd received in my formal training.

I went on to use the model not only in my psychotherapy work, but also in my experience as faculty and speaker in medical school settings, corporate health environments, and public venues. In my work, I realized there were key components of everyday life that were missing or little acknowledged in the model—ones that couldn't or shouldn't be ignored. After going into private practice, I created a more inclusive model of my own, which I originally called the *Whole Health Model*. I used the image of a tree to explain the "branches of health", adding the three branches I knew to be missing at the time: Financial, Interpersonal, and Sexual Health. I later saw the final missing branch—Recreational, which I added to complete the model. It was obvious to me that these additional elements played a major role in understanding an overall sense of "wellness" or "whole health" for patients. I offered the model to clients and professionals as an educational tool to help them understand the interconnectedness of all the branches, which has proven quite effective in helping people re-conceptualize their "holistic" approach to healing. You can't overlook one of the key components of overall health and expect to feel fully balanced—it just doesn't work.

However, the most striking omission to the model was the essence of who each of us are—our unique soul. No other model takes into consideration *who* a person is as they try to reach an optimal or "radiant" life. Working in both wellness and medical fields, I came to realize that the primary void in our modern approach to health is any concern for our soul—the light within us that drives our interest in everything we do. Unlike early conceptualizations of health, our current ones lend very little, if any, value to the influence of our inner self on our everyday lives. Although we are taught to appreciate each individual's views, we are still instructed to follow a more "packaged" approach for how we treat them as clients or patients.

The essence of who we are—the soul—is at the hub of all aspects of our health and well-being. It is the nucleus of every action, behavior, thought, emotion, ache or pain, and it houses an inherent wisdom about what we want and need for optimal health. To treat a patient without a full understanding of who they are as a person is insufficient in treating the "whole" individual. If we only treat the parts, we fail to treat the person and, thus, fail to help them reach optimal and complete vitality.

What I once called the *Whole Health Model* thus evolved into the *Soul Health Model*. As you will read in upcoming chapters, the ten essential elements of the human condition (Physical, Psychological, Social, Interpersonal, Intellectual/Occupational, Financial, Environmental, Spiritual, Sexual, and Recreational) are the keys to balancing our everyday lives; they are the essential ingredients for creating our overall well-being and health. It is blockage to the complex interplay among these elements that often prevents us from reaching complete and deep *soul health*—an overall sense that the various aspects of our lives are aligned with who we are at a core level. The wisdom we need to reach our unique radiance lies within our ability to access our inherent wisdom to determine what we do and don't need in order to heal. In essence, it is our deepest ally; it inspires our path to true health.

As the pandemic went on, I realized that every branch of the model—the tree of life—had been affected in one way or another for all of us. Further into the experience, I realized that not only had the branches been shaken, but the leaves as well! I used the Soul Health Model with all clients, particularly healthcare workers, and realized the importance of writing this book.

Soul Health

As sunlight maintains the entire universe, so the
light of the soul maintains this material body.
—Bhagavad-gita 2.18, Srila Prabhupada

In my previous book, *Soul Health*, I note that to say our soul inspires us is like saying the sun is bright. It is so obvious that even those who acknowledge its existence seldom voice it. In times of darkness—such as the time we have all just experienced, though, it is often difficult to remember that our inner self—our inner light—is the generator of our very existence. When life is out of balance—through stress, a pandemic or any other form of upheaval—it is extraordinarily difficult not to become mired in our human condition. At times, it is nearly impossible to acknowledge that anything other than darkness, exhaustion and discomfort could even exist.

When so much is out of balance, we cannot even hear the innermost inspiration, let alone decipher that we have an inner voice. It is at these times that our overall well-being is most threatened because our internal alert system is shut down and we simply move through life in an automatic manner. When our well-being is fragile or vulnerable, our deepest self is at its lowest potential for evolution; our overall well-being is pretty much nonexistent. However, when we acknowledge the warning signs of imbalance—our depression, anxiety, anger, grief or other "cautions"—that is when we are most likely to grow.

Unlike general wellness models, the Soul Health Model emphasizes the complex and key interplay between our human condition and our inner self, not just a basic approach to life balance shown in other wellness models. Because our personal growth and evolution is dependent on both our overall well-being and a conscious awareness and influence of our deepest self, it is the combination of these forces that is unique to this model.

Financial
Recreational
Interpersonal
Social
Sexual
Psychological
Environmental
Spiritual
Intellectual/
Occupational
Physical

SOUL HEALTH™
M O D E L

In the Soul Health Model, the soul is depicted as the life force within an ever-evolving tree—the part of us that supports and informs us when something is amiss. Much like the growth of an actual tree, which depends on sunlight, clean water and air, our personal evolution—our ability to grow as individuals—depends on the strength of the elements available to it and only thrives when the essentials of our existence are balanced and fulfilled. In the model, these elements reflect the various aspects of our human condition—the wellbeing of our everyday life. Therefore, in order for an individual's inner self to reach unimpeded growth, the individual must consciously maintain this healthy balance. This is not an easy feat given how often and persistently the issues of daily life get in the way, especially when a pandemic comes along to significantly alter our typical path. When we are exhausted and overwhelmed, it is less and less likely that we will hear our inner voice. However, it is through physical, emotional, and other forms of *dis*-ease or lack of contentedness that our soul attempts to get our attention. This inner voice alerts us in order to bring us back into balance and restore a sense of overall wholeness. Only then can we heal and continue to grow.

As depicted in the Soul Health Model, the branches of the tree represent ten primary elements of the human condition: Physical, Psychological, Social, Interpersonal, Intellectual/ Occupational, Financial, Environmental, Spiritual, Sexual and Recreational branches of health. Each branch represents only one key to our overall sense of wholeness and is but one bridge between the human condition and our inner truth. The entire tree represents the interplay between the two and illustrates the detrimental impact even one unhealthy branch can have on your "tree of life's" overall health.

The pandemic left many healthcare workers deeply tattered, wilted or broken. While it might not seem true, an injured, sick or exhausted tree inherently knows what it needs in order to either restore or to sustain overall integrity until healing can take place. This is an automatic process in an actual tree, one that is programmed into the life force of its being so that it will survive and even thrive beyond the impact of the injury. Unfortunately, humans often lack this automatic response or ignore the signs altogether. In this way, we are less conscious of what we need than a tree and often less active in rebalancing our lives. Because our lives are so much more complex than that of a tree, we often miss the cues for when one or more branches of our human condition are threatened and in need of healing. Although we might be more sentient than our woody friends, we are not necessarily wise enough to recognize when or if we need to restore or rebalance.

The 10 Branches of Health

Let me look upward into the branches of the flowering oak and know that it grew great and strong because it grew slowly and well.
—Bill Vaughan

As mentioned, each branch of health represents an aspect of the human condition that affects our overall well-being—each represents something all of us try to balance in our daily lives. Future chapters will describe each branch in greater detail, but for now, become acquainted with what is required for each element to grow strong. Following are brief descriptions of each branch:

Physical: Freedom from physical disease or other signs of ill health. Maintaining this branch includes typical forms of self-care: good nutrition, adequate sleep, basic physical fitness, reasonable mobility, adequate energy and motivation. When we think of health, the physical branch is often most acknowledged; however, the nine branches that follow are equally important in experiencing overall well-being.

Psychological: Freedom from emotional *dis*-ease and the ability to maintain a sense of contentment. A vigorous psychological branch of health includes an overall sense of well-being, self-esteem, positive self-image and of course emotional health—including freedom from depression, anxiety post-traumatic stress, grief or other psychological disturbances. This branch also accounts for our *perception* of the rest of the tree and how balanced our lives really are.

Social: This branch represents the other "beings" that we value in our lives. These include family, friends, partners, pets, neighbors, co-workers, clergy and other individuals with whom we have contact. The important contacts in your life help to create connectedness or community.

Interpersonal: Separate from the Social branch, I emphasize that this aspect of health reflects the *quality* of the relationships we share with others. Interpersonal health includes healthy boundaries, good communication, a good balance of independence and inter-dependence with others (strong give-and-take relationships), mutual respect and equality within one's relationships. Although you may have many social contacts in your life, it is the quality of these relationships that makes the difference.

Intellectual/Occupational: This branch highlights the need for mental stimulation regardless of gainful employment. Intellectual challenge and genuine interest ensure a healthy branch. Engagement in daily tasks, curiosity about people and ideas, acquisition of new knowledge and a general quest for learning enhance this branch of health.

Environmental: Environmental wellness depends on clean, safe, healthy and generally satisfying surroundings, including a comfortable climate, good air quality, reasonable sound regulation, lack of clutter and some degree of control over other external factors that might undermine environmental health and well-being. Important to include, environmental health also includes aspects of the "emotional environment" such as ongoing work stress, family tension and threats to personal safety.

Financial: This branch depends on having ample financial resources to meet our basic needs. There are several ways to maintain this branch: spending within our limits, preventing major debt, saving for the future, investing well, planning for retirement and developing healthy ideas about the use of money. In times of financial crisis, this branch can cause a tremendous impact on every other branch of health. Our beliefs about wealth and abundance also play a part in the vitality of this branch.

Spiritual: This branch of health emphasizes that it takes active and deliberate attention to our spiritual life for our soul to grow, which can be reflected by a sense of inner peace and/or a belief in higher power. Having a healthy spiritual branch doesn't necessarily include the practice of religion. However, it might include regular participation in "centering" techniques such as prayer, meditation and ritual. It might also reflect an unconditional and nonjudgmental mindset toward the rest of the world.

Sexual: Although omitted in other wellness models, this branch plays a key role in overall well-being. It includes healthy sexual boundaries and an understanding of appropriate sexual activity with self and others. Because so many people—women in particular—have experienced sexual trauma, it is important that any such experiences are fully healed in order for the inner self to be unimpeded in its search for peace and ultimate growth. The health of this branch emphasizes a person's ability to see sexual activity as an intimate act of relationship, not simply a way to fill basic, individual needs.

Recreation: Fun and leisure are all too often overlooked as an important part of life. Leisure activities help us to relax and decompress from everyday stress and anything that invokes appropriate laughter and lightheartedness, as well as both physical and emotional release of tension, acts as good medicine. Our society seems to underestimate the value of recreation to our overall health, but a person just has to look at the overall tree to recognize how this branch can enhance a person's general health when other branches are unbalanced.

Peter Wohlleben said, "Evenly formed trees absorb the shock of buffeting forces using their shape to direct and divide the forces through the structure." Just like the Soul Health Model, he emphasized that the balance of a tree's branches is key to withstanding the worst storms. When branches are well-balanced and maintained, the tree can both survive and thrive.

Our Soul's Health and Evolution

The tree of life was always there. Evolution just fills in the gaps.
—Simon Conway Morris

In the illustration of the Soul Health Model, the trunk of the tree represents the soul and is depicted by hands reaching upward toward our most natural state—our inner self's expansive and sustainable evolution. Only when the branches of the tree—our human condition—are in full balance can we freely expand and grow. So, when we experience discomfort about events or situations in our lives, it is our inner self's way of getting our attention and informing us that something is amiss—something is darkening our view and keeping us from fully blooming. Our discomfort is our soul's way of inspiring or alerting us to change—to adjust something within one or more branches or even to prune away what no longer fits. An actual tree doesn't need something to inspire it to change. It just knows there is mending to be done to a broken limb or malnourished trunk. However, humans must learn to view stress, upset, discontent or unhappiness as the signal to assess and balance the key elements of their lives in order to maintain the equilibrium between human condition and the essence of who we are. It is when our growth is impeded or blocked that we feel emotional or physical discomfort, and this leaves us feeling far away from our innate desire to thrive.

Our deepest self inherently knows what we need in order to thrive, but we often get mired in our everyday life—our human condition—to the point where we can't hear it or we ignore the vital cues that are right before us. Understanding the interplay between our overall health—or wholeness—and our inner voice is what can bring our fullest and richest experience of what it means to be human. It can also pave the way on your path to healing.

Preparing for Your Healing Path

In a forest of a hundred thousand trees, no two leaves are alike.
And no two journeys along the same path are alike.
—Paulo Coelho

You will soon begin the process of assessing each branch of health to discover what you do and don't need in your restoration process. You are encouraged to take time to create a path that fits both your preferences and your pace for healing.

Take this into consideration: Anyone who tends to house plants or a garden knows that the two key tricks to keeping plants alive are 1) to clean out the dead or wilting leaves, stems, or branches and 2) to provide water and nourishment to promote growth. These concepts are pretty simple. Unfortunately, our quest for balanced health is often a bit more complicated.

I encourage you to use the Soul Health Model to help you clean out parts of your life that aren't working and to fill up, or enhance, your life by using the influence of your inner self as a guide. It may seem that finding and listening to your inner truth is the more challenging of these tasks in our own evolution. However, in my work as a therapist, it is usually the act of cleaning out unhealthy aspects of the human condition that is often the most challenging part of our growth. This is true because we often become attached to certain people, habits, and objects despite how unhealthy they may be for us.

The ultimate goal is to learn to utilize the voice of your deepest self in the process of balancing the ten essential aspects—or branches—within your life.

Brief Soul Health Survey

Although a full assessment will be offered later in the book, take a moment to complete the following Brief Soul Health Survey. First, take the time to consider how you would have answered prior to the pandemic, then go back and answer again with consideration to how your experience during this difficult time affected you. This will give you some comparison and early information for where to put your focus as you set upon restoring the branches of your tree of life.

In completing the Brief Soul Health Survey, it is not uncommon for individuals to rate themselves higher in overall health, and then re-evaluate when rating their health on each specific branch. This is simply because we tend not to be aware of the interconnectedness of all the branches until we spend time thinking about them individually.

Brief Soul Health Survey

Please circle the number that applies best.

0 represents "not at all healthy" and 10 represents "completely healthy"

Overall Sense of Health
Not at all 0 1 2 3 4 5 6 7 8 9 10 *Completely*

Physical Health
(fitness/exercise, nutrition, lack of disease/illness)
Not at all 0 1 2 3 4 5 6 7 8 9 10 *Completely*

Psychological Health
(emotions, thoughts, self-esteem, lack of *dis*-ease)
Not at all 0 1 2 3 4 5 6 7 8 9 10 *Completely*

Social Health
(friends, family, colleagues, social support, pets)
Not at all 0 1 2 3 4 5 6 7 8 9 10 *Completely*

Interpersonal Health
(personal/family dynamics, communication, boundaries, respect)
Not at all 0 1 2 3 4 5 6 7 8 9 10 *Completely*

Intellectual/Occupational Health
(mental stimulation, occupational fulfillment, curiosity)
Not at all 0 1 2 3 4 5 6 7 8 9 10 *Completely*

Environmental Health
(housing, safety, climate, clutter, sustainability)
Not at all 0 1 2 3 4 5 6 7 8 9 10 *Completely*

Financial Health
(wealth/debt management, planning for future, spending habits)
Not at all 0 1 2 3 4 5 6 7 8 9 10 *Completely*

Spiritual Health
(inner peace, meaning/purpose, belief in higher power)
Not at all 0 1 2 3 4 5 6 7 8 9 10 *Completely*

Sexual Health
(intimacy, passion, safety, satisfaction)
Not at all 0 1 2 3 4 5 6 7 8 9 10 *Completely*

Recreational Health
(leisure, entertainment, relaxation, fun)
Not at all 0 1 2 3 4 5 6 7 8 9 10 *Completely*

Later assessments for each branch of health will help you identify areas of your life that might need to be "trimmed" and others that might need to be "fortified" to promote more growth and fullness of your tree. If your tree of life doesn't feel firmly rooted or grounded, as is often the case following life-altering events, it might be that some foundational work is required to get to know yourself and your values better. This could be particularly true if you feel you've changed at a deep level as a result of your experience during the pandemic. Deep down, we generally know when something isn't quite right; we just don't know how to identify and access whatever isn't working and how to fix it. If this is the case, perhaps now is the time to seek professional assistance to help you explore and heal your inner self in general. The Soul Health Model will help you identify and prioritize what needs attention, but sometimes seeking assistance is what you need to get you started.

Do You Want to Heal or Evolve to An Even Brighter Place?

The creation of a thousand forests is in one acorn.
—Ralph Waldo Emerson

Our soul's most natural state is that of unimpeded growth. The pandemic stopped many in their tracks, but your evolution beyond your challenges depends entirely on your willingness and ability to balance your life in such a way that you create an unobstructed environment for future growth. The inherent wisdom you will learn to access stems from your inner self—the core of who you are, and the only guide that can truly inform you about what you do or don't need on your healing path.

Your soul is an entity of its own—the acorn with endless potential. It yearns to grow and thrive despite the conditions under which it is placed. If left unimpeded, it will gladly create its own expansive inertia—elevating itself until something gets in the way. Many scientists believe that the human body has developed about as much as it is going to. But our inner core—our true self—has infinite potential to grow, shine and ultimately glow once unencumbered by the many unfortunate layers of the human condition. The challenge is that we must commit to healing our discomfort to reclaim our inner light. Only then do we truly evolve beyond what we thought was once impossible.

The following chapters will explore the ten branches of health in much more detail. As you learn more about these key aspects to your health, you will also gain a fuller understanding of how soul health influences and promotes your growth as well, both as a human and as a unique individual.

Before you go on, take a brief moment to use the E.V.O.L.V.E. procedure to revisit the Soul Health Model to:

1. **Examine** what needs to be adjusted first to improve your overall life balance,

2. **Envision** how things could be better,

3. **Observe** what is and isn't working in your life,

4. **Learn** what you can about your experience up to this point,

5. **Venture** into a new perspective or view of how life *could* be, and

6. **Elevate** yourself to a new and brighter level on your healing path.

As you practice using the E.V.O.L.V.E. protocol, you will more readily see how you can move beyond any previously perceived obstacles to living a more radiant life.

CHAPTER SEVEN
THE PHYSICAL BRANCH OF HEALTH
The Body's Roots, Bark and Leaves

Attention to the human body brings healing and regeneration.
Through awareness of the body we remember who we really are.
—Jack Kornfield

In difficult times, many of us forgot who we are—including mind, body and soul. When under stress, unfortunately, one of the first things to get left behind is attention to our basic needs—physical activity, nutrition, rest and various other healthy habits. It is highly likely that the physical branch of health suffers rather quickly when under acute and prolonged stress. Under these conditions, our attention goes to other things. In most cases, and particularly as a healthcare worker in the middle of a pandemic, it is both normal and expected that behaviors associated with physical health will take the first hit. When you think about the interrelated nature of all of your branches of health, you know that when the physical branch feels wilted or broken, it sets the stage for us to lose track of other parts of life as well. Inevitably, the rest of the tree suffers.

84

To healthcare providers who treat others, the physical branch of health is often seen as the most basic and primary focus. However, when you take whole health—or better yet, Soul Health—into consideration, you realize that it is quite multidimensional since it reflects every other branch on the tree.

Now that you have seen the Soul Health Model and casually thought about which branches have been affected as a result of the pandemic, you likely realize there's much more to the story—and more to rebalance and restore as part of your full healing path. Any uncomfortable stirrings you experience as you think about your physical health come from your inner self—the essence of who you are is trying to get you to pay attention to something that needs to be realigned. Remember, we generally only alter our behavior when we are tired of ourselves or our situations. These internal alerts are trying to catch our attention to inform us that it might be time to make changes. If you're thinking along these lines, you are at least in the "contemplative" stage that will eventually lead you to take action.

When I wrote *Soul Health*, I created checklists for each branch of health, not to overwhelm, but to help make a quick assessment of what might be misaligned and need work. Certainly, as healthcare providers, you likely feel there is much to repair following your work during the pandemic. These questionnaires will give you an indication of where to start on your healing path. For now, I recommend you skim through the lists in each chapter, then focus on the branches of health most needing your attention when you actually start your healing plan. Part Three of this book will help you prioritize which areas of your tree of life to work on first. If you prefer, you can wait to complete the questionnaires until you reach that section.

American Philosopher, Henry David Thoreau said, "I'm struck by the fact that the more slowly trees grow at first, the sounder they are at the core, and I think that the same is true of human beings." Keep in mind that personal evolution is a slow process. Once you are firmly on your path to healing, you will gain both commitment and momentum to make the changes necessary to fully brighten your inner light.

To complete the questionnaire: As you read through the questions, listen deeply within for the inner stirrings of your soul. It is the voice that is telling you 1) what needs attention, 2) whether or not you are answering the question honestly, and 3) whether deep down you know that something is unbalanced regarding that particular aspect of your physical health. Sometimes we think we have a good "bill of health", but when we look a little deeper we realize there are a few—or many—areas that need some work. Don't be alarmed by the number of items you check on the list; this awareness simply allows you to identify the elements of this branch that need to be either "cleaned out" or "filled up".

You might want to complete the questionnaire a few times: once to assess how your physical branch of health looked prior to the pandemic, how it looked during or soon after and how you would like it to look once fully on your path to healing. Remember, envisioning a brighter future is part of creating your healing protocol.

While completing the questionnaire, your internal barometer—your inner self—likely influenced how you answered. Any uncomfortable stirrings were reflections of your inner wisdom speaking on behalf of your overall radiant health. For instance, in answering whether you maintain a healthy weight, you may have rated yourself with a low number. Keep in mind that before the pandemic nearly 71% of people in America were already considered to be overweight, so due to additional stressors, eating behavior may have contributed to how you answered this item on the list. Intellectually, we understand what constitutes a healthy weight. However, the responsive stirring you feel within you is your desire to reach or return to a healthy physical weight. Action for this item will take place when your inner self tells you that you are ready. That's how change occurs and generally on its own schedule.

Another example pertinent to your experience with the pandemic is your answer to the questions about personal safety. Everything about safe practices has changed as a result of what we now know about how to care for ourselves and others. This now holds more meaning and currently applies to more than whether you wear a seatbelt or use sunscreen.

Fitness and nutrition are obvious factors in creating and maintaining a strong physical branch of health. However, they are also essential to your overall soul health and personal evolution as a human. When we don't attend to the needs of the body, we also neglect our inner ally. When our body feels healthy, we feel healthy. When it doesn't, we suffer inside as well, not only because physically we are not where we'd like to be, but also because as a result of suboptimal functioning, we are less able to effectively attend to any—or all—other needs.

You are learning that your inner self needs your body to remain well, which helps it to not only survive, but also thrive. It is important to remember that our body is truly the barometer of our overall well-being. If we learn to listen to the cues from within, we can often rebalance our lives for the benefit of our health.

Questionnaire for the Physical Branch of Health

On a scale of 1 to 10, rate the level of your health within each area described. A 10 describes optimal, radiant health, while a 1 describes an almost complete lack of health within the given aspect of the physical branch. Remember, this questionnaire is designed to create a roadmap to overall radiant health. It is not meant to overwhelm you.

Physical Fitness
1._____I am satisfied with the health of my physical body.
2._____I engage in regular physical activity, exercise, and stretching.
3._____I have full and comfortable mobility.
4._____I have enough energy and motivation.
5._____I am fully aware of what my body needs.
6._____My body is strong and vibrant.
7._____I maintain a healthy weight.

Nutrition
1._____I eat healthy and nutritious food daily.
2._____I understand food labels and use them to select what I eat.
3._____I eat a balanced diet with appropriate portion sizes.
4._____I know what vitamins and minerals my body needs and eat food that provides them.
5._____I drink enough water to feel fully hydrated.
6._____I eat when I'm hungry and stop when I'm full.

Sleep
1._____I get enough sleep to feel rested throughout the day.
2._____I sleep deeply and soundly.
3._____I follow a regular sleep schedule.
4._____I am able to sleep without the use of medication.

Illness
1._____I am free of physical illness.
2._____I follow what my healthcare provider recommends to care for my physical health.
3._____I am proactive in preventing illness (self-exams, regular exercise, healthy nutrition, etc.).
4._____I do not have frequent minor illnesses (headaches, colds, infections, injuries).
5._____I take a proactive approach toward returning to health when I am ill.

Healthy Habits
1._____I use no tobacco products.
2._____I drink two or fewer alcoholic beverages per week.
3._____I limit my caffeine intake to the equivalent of two six-ounce cups of coffee per day.
4._____I practice physical safety, using protective equipment such as gloves or goggles when necessary.
5._____I use sunscreen regularly.
6._____I do self-exams as recommended (breasts, testicles, skin, etc.).
7._____I brush and floss my teeth as recommended.
8._____I see all of my healthcare providers as recommended.
9._____I drive safely.
10._____I practice safe sex.
11._____I use non-toxic cleaning and other household products.

Rebalancing Your Physical Branch of Health

Good for the body is the work of the body, good for the soul the work of the soul, and good for either the work of the other.
—Henry David Thoreau

Since the pandemic began, many researchers have tracked its negative impact on physical health. The primary aspects related to COVID that have been researched include weight gain and loss, substance use and relapse, too much or too little sleep and general fatigue. These topics are briefly discussed, mostly to validate what many of you have already experienced.

Weight Gain or Loss

Each year, the American Psychological Association (APA) conducts an on-line survey of individuals in the United States about the biggest stressors experienced during the previous year. Naturally, the 2020 report reflected the emotional impact of the pandemic. But this time, it also indicated many of the physical concerns associated with the stress these individuals felt. The Harris Poll, conducted on behalf of the APA, showed that the majority of US adult survey responders (61%) experienced unwanted changes in weight gain or loss, with an average gain of 29 pounds (10% of adults reporting a gain of more than 50 pounds) and average loss of 26 pounds. Men gained more weight than women (37 pounds vs. 22 pounds) and among essential workers, the average gain was 38 pounds (weight loss average of 30 pounds). Parents showed a 36-pound average weight gain and millennials topped the charts for age ranges (41 pounds). Weight gain was also more prominent for people of color (78% Hispanic, 64% Black, 58% White and 54% Asian). As can be expected, these changes in weight create significant health risks, including higher vulnerability to serious illness from the coronavirus.

Having worked with two weight management programs in separate healthcare systems as well as with numerous individual clients, I'm well aware of the many reasons people use food to cope. Fluctuations in weight can serve as a basic and visible barometer of how someone is doing inside. Depression and concerns with eating go hand-in-hand, since over 75% of those who are diagnosed with problem eating also have depression. Biologically speaking, there is also a clear connection. When upset, most emotional eaters turn toward foods that are high in simple carbohydrates—cookies, candy, ice cream or whatever "sweets" are accessible. Multiple studies show the relationship between carbohydrate intake and subsequent increase in serotonin—the chemical lacking in those who are depressed, increases in dopamine—which activates the reward and pleasure centers, associations with food reinforcement received as children—parents "training" children to want sweet foods when upset by giving them a cookie to calm them, poor monitoring of satiety—physical cues of fullness not registering as a sign to stop eating, and many more pieces to the emotional-eating puzzle.

When the rest of your tree of life is undergoing a major storm, food can provide a quick, but temporary means of finding comfort. However, it can result in long-term consequences that are tough to overcome. Food intake is one of the few things a person can control, especially in the midst of a global health event.

During interviews, many healthcare providers joked about the extra cookies, ice cream or other sweets they indulged in during the pandemic. A few said they had taken the opportunity to exercise more and watch what they ate, but the majority admitted they had lost their focus on healthy eating altogether. Some bounced back to refocus on healthier habits after several months, but few felt they had the time or energy to reset themselves to their pre-pandemic healthy ways. Very few providers reported being where they wanted to be in terms of overall healthy lifestyle. One person who was an avid runner prior to the arrival of COVID noted that she hadn't been jogging more than three or four times since the pandemic began. Most practitioners said they lost access to gyms that had closed for safety reasons, and others said they'd only used their home equipment once or twice in the previous year.

In my experience, people don't usually lose the physical weight until they have worked through and lost the "emotional weight". Because the emotional impact of work during COVID-19 will be ongoing for quite some time, it might be a while before you are ready to address this aspect of physical health.

Sleep

Issues with sleep also spiked during the pandemic, with sixty-seven percent of US adults stating they had slept more or less than desired during the first year. Hispanic adults (78%) were most likely to report changes in sleep, with Black (76%), White (63%) and Asian (61%) individuals reporting significant changes as well.

Sleep is another barometer for whether a person's life is balanced. When stress is high, our neurological pathways "light up", work in over-drive and interfere with the occasions when we usually let go to restore. Between this heightened state and the fact that there is much to think about and process related to our stressful events, good sleep can seem doomed.

The challenge with sleep issues is that many of the other ways we cope, interfere instead. Use of caffeine when fatigued, less physical activity or exercise, poor nutrition and other factors all contribute to poor slumber. Among the more than one hundred healthcare practitioners I interviewed, none reported unaffected sleep.

Substance Use and Relapse

Alcohol use also increased as a method of coping during the pandemic (23% of adults reported drinking more alcohol than in years past), with alcohol sales growing dramatically in the early months of the pandemic (March to June 2020 showed an increase of 34.4%). It also wasn't the "light" stuff people were after: 49.2% of purchases were for hard liquor, and 30.2% beer, malt beverages and cider and 29.1% wine. Overall tobacco sales increased by 13.2%.

While interviewing healthcare providers, several admitted to using alcohol to cope more than they had prior to the pandemic, while others noted they had actually decreased use because they realized it inhibited good sleep. Some noted their alcohol use also decreased because social interactions and family gatherings had been minimal which served as a natural deterrent to popping open a bottle. Two professionals admitted using cannabis to assist in stress relief and sleep induction.

Three main reasons were identified for an increase in alcohol use: 53% of those surveyed used it to cope with generalized stress, 39% to relieve boredom and 32% to alleviate mental health symptoms related to anxiety and depression. In yet another way, the pandemic added multiple layers to our already challenged human condition.

Only one provider I interviewed said he had relapsed from ten years of sobriety, although it is possible others relapsed but chose not to disclose. However, the drug and alcohol literature has made it clear that relapse from sobriety occurred at high rates since very early in the pandemic. Ongoing research and statistics, when available, will show what the true picture holds.

Fatigue

Several organizations printed articles early in the pandemic to explain and address "COVID fatigue" from a healthcare provider perspective, often likening this to combat fatigue experienced when soldiers are at war. Hannah Smith, a psychotherapist, coined the term "Pandemic Fatigue" to describe both the intense tiredness and weariness experienced and the irritability and disorientation that accompany it. This fatigue doesn't only apply to those working in the "front-line" of treating patients, but also for behind-the-scenes workers who were also impacted. One practitioner I interviewed mentioned that their healthcare system's laboratory staff took on COVID testing for their entire region, making these employees responsible for around-the-clock shifts for almost the entire first year testing was available.

Because virtual meetings were scheduled back-to-back, there was often no time in between to "reset". Also, since many relied on the coffee room chat as a social interaction, many felt the loss of this time to debrief with colleagues between patients or meetings, adding to the experience of exhaustion.

Most of the practitioners I spoke with in preparation for this book noted significant and ongoing fatigue. However, I want to provide a differentiation between physical and emotional aspects of exhaustion here. While most researchers and practitioners lump these together, I prefer to separate them for the sake of recovery efforts. Although still a challenge, physical fatigue is far easier to address than emotional fatigue because it is more measurable and tangible—usually occurring from extended activity, insomnia or general lack of sleep. For most, amelioration of physical fatigue requires rest, improved sleep and possibly more balanced nutrition (attention to stimulant intake, nutrients that aid sleep, etc.).

However, emotional exhaustion is far more complicated depending on both the individual's perspective/perception about the event(s) that contributed to the fatigue and the specific factors that caused the weariness. Trauma-based emotional fatigue, whether direct or vicarious, is more complicated to heal than emotional tiredness from simply working long hours in a low to semi-stressful situation. Vicarious grief or multiple grief reactions, extended and intense levels of fear while on the job, "conflict fatigue"—exhaustion from extended and highly intense situations and "listener fatigue"—excessive hours of listening to others discuss troublesome, tragic or traumatic situations, can all take a toll on a person's intrinsic energy reserve. While physical exhaustion is certainly one aspect of COVID fatigue that needs to be addressed, I believe it is the emotional component that will take much more time to heal. Restoration from emotional fatigue doesn't generally occur until the stressful event has long passed, the individual "debriefs" enough from the stressful or traumatic events to lessen the stored load (often through therapy, support groups or general support), he/she grieves or heals from the emotional wounds and the person has an extended period of time to decompress and "air out" without additional major stressors.

One of the primary care providers I interviewed noted that she knows simply a lengthy vacation will not help once she can let down her guard. She added that she wished there was such a thing as a "sabbatical" for healthcare providers available within her medical system. An extended time away from her job is believed to be the only way she could truly recover.

Restoration or Complete Overhaul?

The process of healing does not end when the wounds are no longer visible, it ends when the wounds no longer ache.
—Muskan Sharma

Physical health is a deeply personal thing. Any indication that we are not well threatens the quality or duration of our existence, and, more seriously, it affects the core of our being—the essence of who we are. Because our health is multidimensional, it affects each and every aspect of our lives, which, cannot help but suffer along with the body. Our emotional health often declines when we feel physically ill or unwell. Our relationships can suffer, and in some cases they end. Our work is jeopardized, especially at times when we are overwhelmed, exhausted and burned out—which seemed to be the case for many healthcare providers as they went through the motions of each day during the pandemic. When our physical branch of health is misaligned, we can neglect our surroundings, struggle to find or maintain inner peace (which may go out the window altogether), lose sexual interest and perhaps financial security. In this case, we are certainly not in the right frame of mind to create and enjoy activities that include good fun and leisure. Therefore, when our physical health is challenged, no doubt, the rest of the branches on our tree of life suffer as well.

It wasn't until 1937, when Joseph Pilates published an article in *Your Health* that the mind-body wellness movement became a focus. This was the first time that such a balance was suggested as a means to prevent physical illness through the balance of other aspects of life. However, it still took until 1976 for the National Wellness Institute (NWI) to unveil their six-component model of health.

As noted in the introduction to this book, it took until just fifteen years ago for the Soul Health Model to evolve as well. As I emphasized in the last chapter, the most critical of these aspects is the inherent influence of the soul on each and every other branch of health. Without taking your individual physical needs and challenges into consideration, no one can sustain long-term adjustments nor make permanent changes. Because our inner self is at the very core of our overall well-being, we must address the influences our unique desires, preferences, behaviors, reactions, and responses to all other aspects of life have in order to effectively balance our physical branch as well. In other words, physical health is not "one size fits all"—it is as unique as each individual soul.

Going Beyond Physical Health to E.V.O.L.V.E.

The requirements for our evolution have changed. Survival is no longer sufficient. Our evolution now requires us to develop spiritually.
—Gary Zukov

The word "metaphysical" is often relegated to less researched and respected approaches to healing. However, the word simply refers to anything beyond or transcending ("meta") the physical world ("physics") and our powers of direct perception. Aristotle first coined the term, noting that our human body wouldn't exist without our soul, and vice versa, we cannot separate the wisdom and power of our inner self from that of our physical well-being.

Aristotle also emphasized that metaphysics examines the fundamental nature of reality and being within the world. Clearly, both have changed as a result of the pandemic. Our reality abruptly changed and our way of being in the world will never be the same. This is precisely why your path to healing will require a deeper look. The essence of who you are—who we all are and who we will eventually become—has shifted, but hasn't yet "landed". As each of us examines, envisions, observes, learns, ventures and elevates our reality, we will not only gain clarity, we will also create a restored and brighter future.

As you read through the remainder of this book, you will become increasingly aware of the interrelated nature of all of the branches of health—you can't heal one without the other, and you can't expect to feel fully balanced by leaving some unattended. Although we think of physical health as the primary aspect of vitality itself, it is the collective influence of the other components that constantly interact to create our overall radiance.

When you're ready, look back through the brief questionnaire about physical health provided in this chapter. As a whole, explore your physical branch of health by applying your new E.V.O.L.V.E. protocol and ask yourself the following questions:

E–Examine

- What factors or obstacles are causing disruption or blocking your path to physical health?
- Which aspects of your physical branch of health would be easiest and most realistic to realign?

V–Vision

- When you envision your optimal physical health, how is it different from how you are today?
- How does it feel? How much more energy and "radiance" do you have in this vision?

O–Observe

- How would improving your physical health be *meaningful* to you?
- What is *necessary* to change in order to experience optimal physical health?
- What can you do to *feed your soul* as you work on your physical branch of health?

L–Learn

+ What do you need to learn about physical health to help you thrive? Do you need to learn more about general nutrition? Best methods of exercise? How to create better habits?
+ What can be learned about your methods of coping that might affect your physical branch of health? Can you identify your triggers to eating, drinking or other unhealthy behaviors that take away from optimal physical health?

V–Venture

+ Is there something different or unique you'd like to work on regarding your physical health? A new physical hobby? Take a cooking class? To hire a health coach?
+ What will help you get out of your "norm" when improving your physical branch of health?
+ What new perspective might you need to adopt when thinking about enhancing your physical health?

E–Elevate

+ What would motivate you to make changes in your physical branch of health?
+ Who—or what—might inspire you to improve your overall physical health?
+ What positive words or affirmations do you need to tell *yourself* on a regular basis to create and maintain positive change regarding the physical aspects of your health?

Physical health is but one aspect of radiant living. While components of this branch of health likely need attention to restore you after your experience of the pandemic, other branches may take precedence once you learn about how they all interact.

CHAPTER EIGHT

THE PSYCHOLOGICAL BRANCH OF HEALTH
The Internal Climate

You are the sky. Everything else–it's just the weather.
—PEMA CHÖDRÖN

Buddhist nun, Pema Chödrön is one of the authors I've looked to over the years for healing wisdom, especially when experiencing my own darkest times. A therapist I saw at the end of my graduate education pointed me in her direction. Chödrön's book, *When Things Fall Apart*, became my philosophical handbook as I healed from an unhealthy marriage, issues with my family of origin, challenges I experienced when I was a young teen and even the death of my father seven years prior. She says, "We think that the point is to pass the test or to overcome the problem, but the truth is that things don't really get solved. They come together and they fall apart."

As healthcare providers, we believe that solving problems for others is our job. But when it comes to healing our own, Chödrön emphasizes that we often must "break" in order to repair part of the human experience because, in doing so, we become stronger. She adds, "To be fully alive, fully human and completely awake is to be continually thrown out of the nest... To live is to be willing to die over and over again."

For some healthcare workers, the pandemic has caused various forms of "death" beyond the physical. For those who feel they've been brought to their knees, darkened or even "killed" emotionally, there's little more to do than bounce back up. Sometimes we have to hit our darkest and deepest "down" times in order to turn our lives right-side up.

Chödrön also says that, "The most difficult times for many of us are the ones we give ourselves." I've yet to meet a helper who went easy on themselves and, no doubt, many of you think you should be better off than what you are. But a global pandemic leaves many more casualties among those who are living than those who have passed away. Although it can seem too difficult to embark upon a path to healing after a dark time, when given the directions or plan, our journey can actually enhance and brighten our life. Regarding healing, Chödrön says, "The healing comes from letting there be room for all of this to happen: room for grief, for relief, for misery, for joy." As a psychologist, I know the psychological impact of the pandemic has directly affected every other branch of health, which makes this component the one that will undoubtedly require the most attention.

The True Nature of Nature's Impact

There is something infinitely healing in the repeated refrains of nature —the assurance that dawn comes after night, and spring after winter.
–Rachel Carson

As mentioned in the previous chapter, the American Psychological Association (APA) produces a report about the sources, intensity and stress that people across the United States experience during the preceding twelve months. Their Stress in America 2020 report, of course, focused on how the COVID-19 pandemic profoundly affected Americans. The report started by saying, "We are facing a national mental health crisis that could yield serious health and social consequences for years to come." You, our healthcare providers—those who have been in the trenches, so to speak—already know this, not only because of the upheaval you've seen in your patients, but because of what you experience within yourself as well.

The report revealed a high, but not surprising number of individuals who say the coronavirus pandemic served as a significant source of stress (8 in 10 adults—78%). More than half of those surveyed said their behavior was negatively affected (21% reported increased tension in their bodies, 20% admitted extreme irritability toward someone they love 20% experienced unexpected mood swings and 17% displayed uncharacteristic screaming or yelling at someone close to them). Previously in 2019, health care (66%) and mass shootings (62%) were reported as the highest stressors, which seems quite ironic given that healthcare workers have now been affected so deeply and that mass shootings and other violence has continued even in the midst of this devastating global event.

According to the report, 2 in 3 adults (65%) stated overall uncertainty caused them stress, and 3 in 5 (60%) said the number of issues America faces moving forward overwhelms them. Nineteen percent (1 in 5 adults) state that their mental health was significantly worse than just a year prior, with Gen Z (those between ages 6-21 in 2021) adults reporting the highest percent (34%). Parents reported additional concern, stating that the pandemic made the 2020 school year extremely stressful for both them and their children (63% of all adults, with the highest concern for parents of children aged 8-12, which totaled 76%). Sixty-eight percent of Americans say the political climate was a significant source of stress, which added to the strain already experienced with the pandemic itself.

The good news is that despite the adverse times compounded by the pandemic, 7 in 10 (71%) of Americans still reported feeling hopeful about their future. This proves that the majority of us can still see the light at the end even when the current days may still seem rather dark. As Chödrön alluded to, the weather will eventually improve for you to see the sky—and see *you*—once the storm passes.

Weathering the Storm

*We are like the tiny little branch that quivers during a storm,
doubting our strength and forgetting we are the tree
deeply rooted to withstand all of life's upheavals.*
—Dodinsky

The psychological branch of health is, and will likely always be, the branch of overall health that took the biggest hit during the coronavirus pandemic. Between the "pandemic pandemonium"—the fear, confusion, uncertainty and scramble for basic supplies and needs—and the pervasive emotional impact that will surely persist, we will likely work to heal this branch of our individual soul—as well as that of our collective soul—for quite some time. Mental Health America (MHA), another national organization that addresses psychological health conducted a survey specific to healthcare workers. It is not surprising that ninety-three percent said they were stressed out and stretched too thin, with 86% experiencing anxiety, 77% experiencing frustration, 76% reporting exhaustion and burnout and 75% saying they were overwhelmed. Seventy-six percent said they were worried about exposing someone they loved to the virus and nearly half of healthcare workers reported they struggled with parenting.

Particular to healthcare workers, APA's report also stated that 34% of essential workers received treatment from a mental health worker during the pandemic, with one in four (25%) receiving new mental health diagnoses since the beginning of this historic time. Seventy-five percent said they could have used more emotional support than what they received.

No one has felt the impact of this colossal storm more than healthcare providers and the impact it leaves will likely be massive and long in duration. Many of you will just "get through" as long as you can, but when the time comes, you will need to restore, rebuild and transcend this monstrous event. Three main areas of mental health impact, beyond "simple" anxiety and depression, have already been discussed in recent research: Post Traumatic Stress Disorder (PTSD), Burnout and Compassion Fatigue. I will briefly discuss each, but you likely already know if you experience any or all of these soul-shaking conditions. I will also briefly discuss suicidal ideation, a part of the COVID-19 experience that is often hard to admit. Several of the providers I interviewed disclosed such thoughts and concerns.

Post-Traumatic Stress Disorder

The experience of Post-Traumatic Stress Symptoms (PTSS) began early in the first wave of the coronavirus pandemic. By January 2021, fifty-two journal articles had already been published about the impact of these symptoms on healthcare workers, seventeen of which directly measured the percentage of those who had experienced the signs. In North America, nearly 28% of those surveyed said they experienced nightmares, sleeplessness, intrusive traumatic thoughts, flashbacks, heightened anxiety and emotional shock.

In interviewing various frontline workers, many said they experienced disruption in mood, sleep and ability to interact with loved ones. Some admitted to the emergence of uncharacteristic anger, disinterest in typical interaction with loved ones as well as a noticeable decrease in compassion for others outside of work (family, friends and others who weren't experiencing similar things). Later in the pandemic, many reported feeling post-traumatic stress from the way they were treated by certain patients and colleagues, experiencing hostility from those who lashed out when discussing vaccines and ongoing mask-wearing protocols.

As I mentioned earlier in the book, the subjective experience of fear is usually the primary emotion that precipitates a PTSD or PTSS reaction. Most people who experience severe PTSD have previously experienced serious life-threatening conditions in their lives—war and other forms of physical violence, rape and other forms of sexual violation, accidents, natural disasters or other deeply impactful events. In the case of the pandemic, not only did the visual impact of seeing so many others suffer impact healthcare workers, but also the fear associated with not being able to save them cut deeply. A healthcare practitioner's professional identity is often closely tied to helping others. However, when providers perceive themselves as failing to do so—sometimes repeatedly even in one shift—this takes a serious and profound toll. The deepest part of a healthcare provider—the essence of who they are, their soul—can easily become deeply scarred.

A paramedic I interviewed admitted that his work during the pandemic was affected by trauma he experienced while serving in Iraq. After several months of working the "front lines" of the pandemic, the trauma took its toll and he had to take time off from work to seek help. He mentioned that this time around, the trauma felt much worse given the residual effects of his previous suffering.

While reviewing articles related to COVID-19 associated PTSS, I came upon a promising study that measured "Post-Traumatic Growth" (PTG) in US veterans who had also contracted the virus. It showed that among other things, veterans experienced greater appreciation of life, improved social relationships and increased personal strength following their recovery from the virus. Although not directly related to the experience of healthcare workers, it is possible that many providers will experience positive growth, a more positive long-term effect of the pandemic. This will likely take place after the initial healing is complete, but nevertheless, something positive may come from the healing process.

Acknowledgement of PTSD or PTSS is difficult for healthcare providers who want to remain viable and strong for those they help. This is where your work around Soul Health comes in. To fully heal from your coronavirus experience, it is important to not only address the traumatic symptoms, it is necessary for you to understand how it affected you at the deepest level. This understanding will facilitate your healing and help you more fully restore beyond the experience.

Burnout

Numerous studies have also been published regarding burnout in healthcare providers since early in the pandemic. In the Mental Health America survey, emotional exhaustion was the most common answer (82%) for changes in how healthcare providers were feeling over the previous few months. In an article targeting burnout among female healthcare workers, it was found that structural factors—work-related policies, staff shortages and access to personal protective equipment were a primary force of stress and burnout during COVID-19. Sixty-six percent of female coworkers also reported that safety concerns and fears of getting infected and putting family members at risk significantly contributed to the burnout they experienced. Researchers highlighted that some women may have been more susceptible to burnout if they were young with no family or mothers with young children. They noted that recently graduated providers might also have been more vulnerable given that they have less time on the job and may perceive themselves to lack the competency that comes with experience.

One article that discussed burnout in women added that calling female healthcare workers "heroes" might actually increase stress and burnout because to be called a hero can increase moral responsibility and stress to meet these expectations; but with increased isolation and stigma many were considered as "contagious" by the general population.

In my interviews with healthcare providers, very few noted the absence of burnout regardless of age, gender or ethnic group. One provider said, to her, burnout was a given so she no longer thought of it as anything unusual anymore. A male medical educator said that although he understands burnout, he feels more comfortable with the term mental fatigue, adding that it feels more vulnerable and "clinical" to admit to more.

As I mentioned in the Physical Branch of Health chapter, I believe that emotional exhaustion is far more difficult and takes more time to heal than physical exhaustion. As an example, a study from a decade ago indicated that American adults have approximately sixty thousand thoughts a day, two-thirds of which are negative thoughts. Because the pandemic forced us to think and even "overthink" so many things, our brains worked in overdrive just to get through a day. Healthcare workers, who are expected to make decisions on the spot, likely had exponentially more thoughts than even the average citizen who already had an elevated number of thoughts to process. Add this all together and you easily get over-worked brains along with the body that put in long, stressful shifts. I will talk more about how to heal emotional fatigue in Part Three of this book as part of the overall protocol to post-COVID recovery. For now, just take into consideration that healing from burnout is likely a significant part of your healing path.

Compassion Fatigue

Compassion fatigue is known as the deep emotional and spiritual exhaustion that accompanies acute emotional pain. It should be noted that we could also experience compassion fatigue when observing others who experience sustained emotional discomfort—a form of vicarious trauma. Early in the pandemic, researchers surveyed healthcare workers to determine the initial impact of their work. The term, Rapid Onset Compassion Fatigue (ROCF), was used to describe what front-line workers experienced. Being other-directed, as healthcare workers are, can quickly lead to the development of key symptoms: depersonalization (feelings that you are an outside observer of your thoughts, feelings and even your body), irritability, feelings of self-contempt, difficulty sleeping, weight loss, headaches and indifference to friends, loved ones, coworkers and/or the line of work itself.

Several of the healthcare providers I spoke with admitted experiencing compassion fatigue, mostly toward friends, loved ones and some coworkers, not their patients. In fact, most stated that working with COVID-19 patients actually increased their sensitivity toward the patients they served, although they were often dismayed by unvaccinated individuals who contracted the virus. Many said seeing COVID-19 patients actually made them better providers. However, several admitted that they had become more irritable, distant or insensitive toward those in their personal lives. One traveling ICU nurse noted that he had not spoken to several of his friends and a few family members in quite some time because their stress seemed so insignificant compared to what he experienced every day.

No doubt, healthcare workers are faced with the challenges of burnout and compassion fatigue regardless of an event such as a pandemic. Perhaps what you learn in your healing process will assist you not only in your post-COVID recovery, but also in the years thereafter.

Suicidal Ideation

Although no one likes to talk about suicide, healthcare practitioners in particular have a difficult time admitting when their light has dimmed so much that they'd rather extinguish it completely. While suicide has been on the rise for the last twenty years, at the time this book was written, no clear statistics were available to illustrate whether the pandemic had caused a spike. Early in 2020, a medical psychiatry journal said the pandemic created "a perfect storm" for increased risk due to the social isolation, increased financial distress, decrease in access to mental health care, loss of support through community or spiritual organizations, illness and medical problems, high national and international anxiety, an increase in firearm sales and the intense stress frontline healthcare workers experience.

A few of the providers I interviewed disclosed suicidal thoughts while working during the pandemic, while many admitted to high levels of depression and anxiety as well as newly diagnosed conditions. No providers reported knowing someone in their institutions who had committed suicide, but one medical school administrator did share he had heard of a medical practitioner in his facility who took his own life. As a psychologist, I'm aware that most people don't really want to end their lives, they just want to stop feeling the pain or discomfort they experience. Because of the depth in which this world event has impacted healthcare workers, it is imperative that we access the care needed to address this issue, regardless of personal or professional stigma that might still be present. The problem is that if someone's light has grown so dim that they want to take their life, these individuals might not feel they have the resources to do the healing work to relight their flame. Know that there is light beyond the darkness.

If you or someone you know is experiencing suicidal thoughts, call the 24/7 National Suicide Prevention Lifeline at 1-800-273-8255 or go to https://suicidepreventionlifeline.org/.

No matter the impact on the psychological branch of health, the health of this branch is essential in healing all other aspects of your human condition.

The Psyche and Soul Health

There is no coming to consciousness without pain. People will do anything, no matter how absurd, in order to avoid facing their own Soul. One does not become enlightened by imagining figures of light, but by making the darkness conscious.
—Carl Jung

In my book, *Soul Health*, I say that while the body is the barometer of the soul, the psyche is its voice. When we experience an emotion, it is the cue that something is not quite right in our world—something needs to be realigned so we can come back into balance. But what happens when you're so overwhelmed or numb that you don't recognize when something is amiss?

The psychological branch of health includes any emotional concern we might have—anxiety, depression, grief, stress, trauma and post-traumatic stress, burnout, emotional fatigue and more, as well as *perceptual* concerns such as issues with self-esteem, body image, self-efficacy, confidence and an overall sense of well-being. If we fail to hear or address what our inner self is trying to tell us about how we are feeling inside, we might manifest physical symptoms instead (headaches, intestinal issues, muscle tension and so on). Thus, our inner self tries to send a louder message through our physical discomfort, often ones we cannot ignore in the forms of discomfort, pain or illness. So, to experience fully balanced soul health, we must understand that our psyche is often in charge of either creating or denying it.

John Steinbeck, a Pulitzer Prize winner, wrote, "A sad soul can kill quicker, far quicker, than a germ." It was through an emergence from his own dark nights that he came to understand how the human condition could become immobilized when an individual is engulfed in heavy emotion. To make a basic assessment of your overall psychological branch of health, take the following questionnaire. Remember that each emotional concern you identify provides the information you need to realign your life; each provides the insight you need to move beyond your discomfort and get you firmly situated on your healing path. Just as with the Physical Branch of Health Questionnaire, consider exploring your overall psychological health prior, during and after the pandemic. Then envision how you would like this branch to feel in the years to come. This ability to envision a brighter future is essential in making full psychological health a reality.

The brief questionnaire for the psychological branch of health provides some basic information about what needs to be restored and rebuilt on your path to healing. Keep in mind that you don't need to change anything until you are ready; this exercise is simply meant to help you identify what needs attention. Further assistance in creating your overall healing plan is offered later in the book as you learn how to put all of the information together.

Questionnaire for the Psychological Branch of Health

On a scale of 1 to 10, rate the level of your health within each area described. A 10 describes optimal, radiant health, while a 1 describes an almost complete lack of health within the given aspect of the psychological branch. Remember, this questionnaire is designed to create a roadmap to overall radiant health. It is not meant to overwhelm you.

Stress
1._____I recognize and can acknowledge the stressors in my life.
2._____I know how to manage my stress in ways that enhance my overall health.
3._____I am open to professional help when stress overwhelms me.
4._____I proactively engage in activities that help to reduce or prevent stress.
5._____I am aware of how my emotional stress affects other aspects or branches of my health.

Psychological Concerns
1._____I am free of depression and ongoing sad thoughts.
2._____I am free of worrisome or anxious thoughts.
3._____I have good overall psychological health.
4._____I know when and how to seek professional help for any psychological concern.
5._____I willingly seek professional help for psychological concerns.
6._____I engage in proactive behaviors that enhance my psychological health.
7._____I can identify and express the full range of my emotions.
8._____I handle my emotions in a healthy way.
9._____I concentrate well on tasks I undertake.
10._____I face my fears.

Self-Esteem
1._____I like—and even love myself.
2._____I know and accept my worth.
3._____I have only positive thoughts about myself.
4._____I know and accept who I am.
5._____I am self-confident.
6._____I am successful in most areas of my life.

Self-Awareness
1._____I know my strengths and weaknesses.
2._____I can accurately describe how I impact others.
3._____I am generally self-aware.
4._____I am able to identify the source of my emotional concerns quickly.
5._____I actively work to be self-aware and to learn about myself.
6._____I have healthy emotional boundaries.

Perceptions
1._____I have a positive outlook on life.
2._____I am open to all that life has to offer.
3._____I can accurately describe things that happen around me.
4._____I see the world as a good place.
5._____I understand and accept that people have ideas and beliefs different from my own.
6._____My perceptions of myself match what others think of me.

For now, explore what needs to be healed and changed to improve
your psychological health by applying your new E.V.O.L.V.E. protocol.
Ask yourself the following questions:

E–Examine

- In what ways has my psychological health been impacted as
  a result of my work during the pandemic?
- What factors existed prior? Are the differences apparent?
- Which aspects of my psychological branch of health am I
  ready to address, heal and realign?

V–Vision

- Can you envision healing or evolving *beyond* the emotional
  state in which the pandemic left you?
- What would life look like if you healed? How would it be
  different? How does it feel?
- What wounds, obstacles or other hindrances need to be left
  behind?

O–Observe

- How aware are you of how you handle emotions?
- What is *necessary* to heal in order to experience optimal
  psychological health?
- Are there areas of your psychological health that you are
  avoiding?

L–Learn

- What did you learn about yourself during the pandemic
  related to your psychological health?
- What can be learned about how previous stressors affected
  how you coped?
- Who or what can help you to grow and heal now?

V—Venture

- Do you need to venture into new methods of improving your psychological health? Seek a therapist, attend a support group or enroll in some online classes you wouldn't previously have attended?
- How does my willingness to be vulnerable help or hinder my healing within the psychological branch of health?
- What new perspective might you need to explore when thinking about healing your psychological health?

E—Elevate

- What obstacles do I need to overcome regarding my psychological health in order to elevate my mood or way of coping?
- What will encourage me to keep moving forward when all I want to do is hide under a rock?
- What is the most encouraging thing I need to say to myself as I embark on healing my psychological branch of health?
- I'm biased—I think everyone needs a therapist to help him or her through life. We all have blind spots and areas of life we'd rather ignore. But healing our psychological concerns and wounds is essential in rising above them. We certainly don't appear radiant on the outside when our internal world remains dim.

CHAPTER NINE

THE SOCIAL BRANCH
OF HEALTH
The Forest and the Trees

But the most astonishing thing about trees is how social they are.

—PETER WOHLLEBEN

L ike trees, humans are social beings. We need one another to both
survive and thrive. But when you add a pandemic to the mix,
everything in our social nature and structure is shaken, altered and
sometimes even broken.

Each soul-to-soul connection we share has a direct impact on overall
health—each one influences the essence of who we are. Although the
vast majority of people come to therapy because of the relationships
in their lives, the social impact of COVID-19—both during and
after—created an unusual and added strain. Every single healthcare
practitioner I interviewed for this book noted a change in her or his
social health, both at home and at work. When our primary support
systems are lacking, absent—or even eliminated, this branch of health
suffers.

George Bernard Shaw said, "We are all dependent on one another, every soul of us on earth." But what happens when those we depend on are out of reach, unsupportive or share different views and values? No doubt, our social health diminishes and we can be left to fend for ourselves—physically, psychologically, interpersonally, financially and so on. Although I mentioned the psychological branch of health would likely be the most deeply and sustainably damaged branch on the tree, it often comes as a result of the social aspects of our experiences triggering the emotional response. This is just one more example of how interrelated the branches of health really are.

All of the relationships in our lives comprise the social branch of health—those close to us such as family, partners/spouses, friends and even pets, and also those we might interact with less frequently or intimately—neighbors, store clerks, clergy, mail carriers, our own medical providers, massage therapists, fitness trainers, coffee baristas, bankers and more. Interestingly, for many healthcare providers the pandemic created more of a reason to bond with coworkers or other health-related professionals than in the past. Because most human behaviors take place in social contexts, interactions with others are often considered the most important experiences in daily life. In terms of our personal evolution, it is most often how we learn and grow as a result of our interactions with others that determines how far we go. Directly related to the pandemic, one provider said, "This is not just a shared experience", noting that the changes she saw in social structure pervaded every aspect of life as she knew it.

While U.S. adults are said to have approximately twelve social interactions a day, this varied widely when the pandemic was at its height, sometimes for better or for worse. This means there were countless opportunities to learn more about our social branch of health during this challenging time.

Soul-to-Soul Connections

Our souls speak a language that is beyond human understanding.
A connection so rare the universe won't let us part.
—Nikki Rowe

Our soul health is often a direct reflection of the company we keep. While we crave connection with others, we need more than just another human body in our lives to feel fulfilled. To have a vibrant social branch of health, it is necessary for our interactions to be meaningful and they need to feed our souls. These relationships must enhance instead of diminish our lives. Otherwise, these connections can be more of a liability to soul health than an enhancer of it. The ability to maintain our own inner light depends on whether the light in others can help to sustain us.

The pandemic created many challenges to the social branch of health. Not only did the imposed social isolation make it impossible for many to have the contact with others they needed, but often the social interactions we did have were less than nourishing. While "collective resilience", or the tendency of groups banding together to overcome a difficult time, came into play, many said that the differences in beliefs and values also sometimes created fractures in previously established bonds.

In my book *Soul Health*, I discuss the difference between life-affirming and life-diminishing relationships. As already mentioned in this book, people carry energy—or light—within them which can either be bright or dim, depending on the health of their soul. When we interact with people who are life-affirming, we feel positive, light, joyful and energized; these connections have a "life-giving" quality to them. However, life-diminishers can leave us feeling heavy, depleted and drained; these individuals can be life-draining while in their presence. Life affirmers have healthier and brighter souls, while the life diminisher's souls are dim, damaged or broken. Because the experience of the pandemic was already so draining and "dimming" to our inner light, our ability to maintain a vibrant social branch of health was already compromised. If the people in your life were also draining and life-diminishing, it was likely difficult or even impossible to sustain your own light during this challenging time.

Another common challenge noted by both clients and the health practitioners I interviewed was the almost immediate rifts that developed between themselves and friends or loved ones because of differing views and values placed on social distancing, mask wearing and vaccines. As a therapist, I spent numerous hours helping clients come to terms with their changing relationships due to these reasons. In therapy, I often say that the older we get, the more discerning we need to be with whom we choose to spend our time. However, the pandemic accelerated this discernment process with healthcare practitioners of all ages as the differences between themselves and those they love were quickly revealed.

Interviews with healthcare workers exposed changes in social health early in the pandemic. Many practitioners distanced themselves from family, friends and neighbors when they observed them dismissing both science and the mandated restrictions. Other providers felt ostracized or ousted from their homes and communities either because of their cautious views or because partners, family or friends considered them as risks to their own health and well-being. Many others expressed frustrations with neighbors, whom they observed intermingling despite social distancing mandates. Some even expressed frustration when colleagues didn't share similar views about how to care for themselves or others. Several reported added stress in relationships due to shifting roles within the household since many non-medical spouses had to pick up the slack for those who were overwhelmed by their frontline status. Divorces, separations, affairs and broken friendships were only some of the social casualties mentioned by healthcare providers.

All scenarios of separation from those we once considered to be our main supporters damaged the social branch of health. Some "branches" were left temporarily wounded, while others broke completely.

Several practitioners who worked in private practice expressed extreme isolation since their "private" status was magnified once required to work virtually. A psychologist from New York City said he felt severe isolation when he was forced to close a thriving practice with multiple colleagues and move his office home. He added that he felt his social skills were waning because he spent no time interacting socially, other than with his immediate family who were living within the small household. Between the heavy emotional work he did with clients in one of the U.S. epicenters of the pandemic and the loss of collegial interaction and support, he admitted returning to therapy, himself, to help cope with the changes he had undergone.

Another psychologist from a large city in the southern United States said, "The things we get from each other aren't quantifiable." Regarding teletherapy with clients, she added that she often thought, "I've seen you every week, but I haven't actually seen you at all." She went on to say that she has observed a pervasive social phenomenon emerge since people now see others as dangerous, noting that this sensation makes you feel you must stay away from them altogether. She added, "As a society we are losing out. We don't have the 'felt' experience that you get when you are in the presence of others, so people no longer know how to feel okay or safe." Clearly, this will create a long-term negative impact on the social branch of health, one that may be difficult to heal.

Some practitioners noted a significant shift in their collegial support because of coworkers either being laid off and/or furloughed or choosing to leave their jobs altogether. Several providers from throughout the United States and Canada estimated they lost up to thirty-five percent of their unit or department staff. Some added that their collegial interactions began to feel transient with the comings and goings of traveling nurses and other temporary healthcare professionals. They never even attempted to bond with the new employees.

Still others expressed grief about the loss of spiritual or religious networks because they hadn't been able to attend in-person services or because of how some of these establishments handled social distancing and mask-wearing. One practitioner stated that her disappointment in the congregation's approach to caring for themselves was too great to continue her membership in her church. Other providers throughout the country shared similar stories.

Many holistic health providers reported extreme isolation since these practitioners already tended to occupy office spaces. Many either had to close their practices or move to an even smaller and more affordable space. One Ayurvedic practitioner said she gained a greater appreciation for building a holistic community and is now working more intentionally to maintain contacts with other natural health providers. A naturopathic physician moved her practice home to save on overhead expenses. She was concerned for the risk of exposure since her mother had a compromised immune system related to ongoing cancer treatment. She also had two young children at the time and suddenly became the primary caregiver, which further altered her ability to practice client work. Massage therapists, energy workers, chiropractors, reflexologists and many other holistically-based practices halted or shut down completely during the pandemic, which created a large gap in social connection.

Along with the reports of strained social connections, many practitioners expressed gratitude for relationships that were strengthened as a result of the pandemic. Most expressed that they had become much more intentional about the positive and supportive relationships in their lives. They either had to lean on one another more or so much time passed between interactions with these support persons that they wanted to take every opportunity to connect. Many healthcare workers were able to spend unexpected "bonus" time with their children of all ages since they were home from school. Some reported renewal of fondness for their partners or spouses. One physician said she actually felt closer to her husband than she had in ten years, but wasn't really sure why. Numerous providers showed appreciation for their medical colleagues, either because they were inspired by their actions or because they had become closer while supporting one another.

Although it might seem unlikely for someone to find a new love interest in the middle of a pandemic, a few practitioners said they had met someone with whom they developed a strong romantic bond. One physician assistant reported that her personal life had begun to develop at the beginning of the outbreak and she became engaged and married to the love of her life just over a year into the health crisis. Other practitioners felt the time had brought them closer to other medical professionals, some with whom they became romantically partnered.

Personally, as a result of writing this book, I reconnected with several colleagues from around the country, some I hadn't spoken to since I attended graduate school over twenty-two years ago. One such medical colleague joked that it took a pandemic for us to reconnect after I called to interview him for this book. Others have asked me to visit their facilities once it to safe to do so to offer staff retreats and trainings based on recovering from their work during COVID.

Whether the storm of the pandemic enhanced or diminished the social branch of health for a healthcare practitioner, the changes still profoundly affect the overall tree—the overall health of the individual.

Conscious and Soulful Connections

If I accept the fact that my relationships are here to make me conscious, instead of happy, then my relationships become a wonderful self-mastery tool that keeps realigning me with my higher purpose for living.
–Eckhart Tolle

One of the things I told clients at the beginning of the pandemic was that this event would make us more discerning about those with whom we choose to spend our time. That statement held truer than even I knew it would since so many clients and healthcare providers noted significant changes in their social branch of health. When teaching clients and workshop participants about how to assess the "health" of a relationship, I remind them of the Three Questions of Discernment described in Chapter Four. I encourage people to ask themselves: 1) "Is the relationship meaningful?" 2) "Is it necessary?" and 3) "Does it feed your soul?" Certain connections may fit all or none of these criteria. It is up to you to decide when it is time to redefine, enhance or eliminate a relationship in your life. It is possible that your experience during the pandemic has shifted your priorities about who stays and who goes.

Another reminder for clients is that our relationships provide the primary opportunities to grow and evolve. Our interactions with others—whether pleasant or not—make us more aware of areas of our life that need work. Essentially, the people in our lives help to illuminate which branches of health may need some attention. We just have to be open enough to recognize we might need some work and to commit to being intentional enough to follow through. Our personal evolution often depends on the relationships we share with others. It also depends on our willingness to assess whether these relationships facilitate or inhibit our growth. Along with reminding people of the *Three Questions of Discernment*, I also offer a three-step assessment for whether the connections in a person's life are "conscious"—whether there is an *awareness* of the health of a relationship, while remaining sensitive to the needs of your inner self.

Although many of the relationships we have in our lives are "ready-made"—parents, siblings and other family ties, all connections we hold require some sort of assessment for the "health" which they bring to our social branch of health. This helps us to maintain, enhance, redefine or eliminate relationships according to the needs of our social branch of health. Without this conscious assessment, our connections might feel unsatisfying or empty—or might even damage our overall health if left unattended.

Through over three decades of doing therapy, I have recognized that although many models of healthy relationships exist (which encourage the development of trust, honesty, communication, etc.), the healthiest, most fulfilling and sustainable relationships display three main "conscious" characteristics: Connectivity, Intentionality and Explicit

Reality. I'll explain each to assist in assessing the health of your social connections to further determine which ones might need some attention.

Connectivity

We might have many people in our lives, but what makes a relationship meaningful is the shared interests that help us to really connect. Author, Donna Goddard says, "There is a depth to life which only comes from our connection to other people." We feel the closest to those whom share our views, likes and dislikes, but we often feel most connected to those who have either shared or at least can understand our challenges within the human condition—including our experiences during the pandemic.

While we might feel connected to individuals in our lives when we first meet, it is possible to grow apart over time. Unless we can find and maintain our points of connection, we often drift away from those we once considered essential to us. Sometimes you can rekindle your shared interests, but sometimes you cannot. Either way, our connections with others are a primary source of learning about ourselves—a key part of both our individual and social evolution.

Intentionality

Intentionality, or living with deliberate and purposive action, is somewhat of a new term when applied to relationships. Prior to a few decades ago, "couple" behavior was directed more toward a common goal—having and raising kids or just for the sake of being in a relationship—rather than for establishing and maintaining a deep bond with one another. However, as we have developed as a society, our needs within relationships have changed as well, requiring more intentional selection of a partner as well as more intentional behavior to build and sustain the connection once a partner is chosen. In family relationships, friendships, work relations and any other meaningful connections, intentionality plays a vital part in whether or not our social branch remains healthy.

Author, John Maxwell said, "An unintentional life accepts everything and does nothing." Relationships that lack intention do nothing but harm the health of our overall tree. With respect to the social branch of health, the absence of intentionality within a relationship can be detrimental both to the individual and the relations they hold. The trick within conscious connections is to hold true to oneself to maintain your sense of self—the essence of who you are—while remaining intentional about creating and maintaining ongoing, healthy bonds with those in your life. If one or both people within a relationship lack intentionality toward the connection, something will no doubt need adjustment or the connection will fade or break.

Explicit Reality

If "explicicity" were a word, I would use it to describe what I think most relationships lack the most—the willingness to share explicitly what they need or how they feel within any given relationship. How often do you hold back sharing clearly and openly what is really going on inside of you? And how often does the other person—a partner, family member, friend, coworker or other—make a false assumption as a result or take it personally that you are withholding information?

Most communication issues arise because someone hasn't fully and clearly expressed what they want, need or require in order to stay strongly connected. Resentment builds, bonds are dissolved, damaged or broken and souls subsequently part ways. It is true that sometimes a need is expressed and the other person involved ignores the request—this is simply necessary information for a determination whether that person can give you what you need. But if your thoughts, needs and perspective are never shared then the responsibility is yours for not having spoken up. Often, we may try to avoid conflict, believing the other person can't handle what we have to say. We may also avoid speaking up because we may not feel worthy of getting our needs met. A relationship that lacks the willingness or ability to be explicit also lacks a sustainable bond that will get you through even the worst of times—especially a pandemic.

During the mid-1800's, Prime Minister of the U.K., Benjamin Disraeli, alluded to the unfortunate truth that people aren't accustomed to sharing openly by stating, "Frank and explicit—that is the right line to take when you wish to conceal your own mind and confuse the minds of others." We are so unused to sharing the truth of our inner self that we don't even realize we aren't sharing it at all. Each omission of truth—each misalignment from our deepest self—impacts our overall soul health and diminishes our light.

Humans need one another to thrive and survive. All social connections are essential to our evolution, but it is when we unite with healthy souls through connectivity, intentionality and our explicit reality that we reach our greatest potential for overall radiant health.

The Reckoning of Relationships

A healthy relationship will never require you to sacrifice
your friends, your dreams or your dignity.
—Mindy Hale

The interpersonal branch of health, which will be discussed in the next chapter, more deeply explores the richness and quality of relationships you hold. For now, allow yourself to discover if you have too few or too many connections to maintain or enhance your social health.

Take the following questionnaire to assess your social health more thoroughly. Similar to the previous questionnaires, decide if it is helpful to make a social health assessment pre-, during and post-pandemic. This will give you a better idea of how this branch of health has been impacted.

Questionnaire for the Social Branch of Health

On a scale of 1 to 10, rate the level of your health within each area described. A 10 describes optimal, radiant health, while a 1 describes an almost complete lack of health within the given aspect of the social branch. Remember, this questionnaire is designed to create a roadmap to overall radiant health. It is not meant to overwhelm you.

Social Contacts

1._____I have enough social support.
2._____I have close friends.
3._____I am close to my family.
4._____Pets are an important part of my social network.
5._____I know the names of my neighbors.
6._____I enjoy my co-workers and/or fellow students.
7._____I am often around like-minded people.
8._____I am generally friendly toward others.
9._____I develop new relationships easily.
10._____I am satisfied with the number of people in my life.
11._____I am aware of how my relationships affect other aspects or branches of health.

Time

1._____I spend enough time with friends and family.
2._____I socialize with friends at least once a week.
3._____I live close enough to family.
4._____I look forward to spending time with friends and family.
5._____I talk frequently with my friends.
6._____I talk frequently with my family.
7._____I have at least one friend who lives in my town or city.

Quality

1._____I like the people in my life.
2._____I share many interests with the people in my life.
3._____I feel safe and at ease in my friendships and relationships.
4._____I value the many of the same things as my friends and vice versa.
5._____I feel proud to be friends with those in my life.
6._____I feel proud to be part of my family.
7._____My friends know who I really am.
8._____My family knows who I really am.
9._____I only spend time with people who are healthy for me.

Relationship with Self

1._____I enjoy spending time alone.
2._____I know when I need time alone.
3._____I know when I need time with others.
4._____I have interests that can be done alone as well as with others.
5._____I don't generally get lonely.
6._____I am a healthy influence for those in my life.
7._____I love myself enough to only allow healthy souls into my life.

When it feels right to review your social health, consider whether your connections with others are built on connectivity, intentionality and explicit reality. Then, take another look at the Questionnaire for the Social Branch of Health. Think about how you can "clean out" or "fill up" your social branch by applying the E.V.O.L.V.E. protocol:

E–Examine

+ What has changed about your social health since the beginning of the pandemic?
+ What needs to shift about your social health to enhance this branch? (Perhaps through exploring whether your relationships are built on connectivity, intentionality and explicitly sharing with others.)
+ What needs to be "cleaned out" and "filled up" as part of fortifying your social health?

V–Vision

+ How do you envision your social health in the future?
+ What kinds of people (and pets!) are ideal for creating a vibrant social network?

O–Observe

+ How have your interactions changed with the people in your life?
+ What is meaningful and necessary about your relationships?
+ Do those in your life feed your soul?

L–Learn

+ What have you learned about yourself in terms of what you need for a healthy social branch of health?
+ What can you learn about how you choose the people you allow into your social circle?
+ What types of relationships have you outgrown?

V–Venture

+ Do you need to find a new social group?
+ What types of activities could you add to your social calendar to meet new people or enhance the relationships you already have?
+ What would help you build confidence to meet new people?

E–Elevate

+ What gets in your way from getting to know new people? How can you overcome these obstacles?
+ Do you need to "level up" with the types of people or crowds you choose?
+ How can you step outside your comfort zone to widen your social network?

CHAPTER TEN

THE INTERPERSONAL
BRANCH OF HEALTH
The Soul's Connections

Soul connections are not often found and are
worth every bit of fight left in you to keep.
—Shannon L. Alder

We always learn the most about ourselves through our interactions
with others. While the social branch of health explores the roles
others play in our life, the interpersonal branch of health helps you
examine the quality or richness that each person offers in day-to-day
living. You may think that having many people in your life indicates
good social health, but if the interpersonal nature of those connections
is life-draining, your interpersonal branch of health may be unhealthy,
causing harm to your overall tree of life.

The pandemic created many new interpersonal dynamics between
us and loved ones as well as exacerbating already existing social under-
currents. While the health crisis created stronger bonds between some
healthcare workers and their social connections, the extreme stress often
created new challenges for otherwise healthy relationships while making
previously unattended issues much less avoidable. Many providers noted

added stress in relationships with partners and spouses—some due to shifting roles with household responsibilities such as childcare, while others mentioned strain with other relationships, including extended family, friends, neighbors and coworkers. Some providers stated concerns were already present while a few felt the pandemic was the sole cause of their separations or divorce. Several providers said they had to set strict boundaries with family members and friends outside their household who weren't observing social distancing guidelines or mandates. They noted that strain and even newfound disrespect settled into the relationships as a result.

Regarding changing dynamics with coworkers, one family medicine provider said she'd never seen so much conflict among her colleagues as she did when the pandemic was at its height. An administrator of a drug and alcohol treatment center said she had to intervene with bickering staff members almost daily because the added stress they were under stripped them of previously congenial demeanors. An emergency room nurse said she felt condemned by fellow coworkers because she tried to stay to herself to manage her stress. Her supervisor reprimanded her for not being a team player.

Self-awareness is particularly important to interpersonal health, not only because this consciousness helps you to better understand how you handle stress, but because it helps you understand how you react to the strain of others as well. If you consider yourself to be an introvert, you might handle the pressures of a global health crisis differently than if you are more outgoing. If you have past trauma, depression, anxiety, relationship or other concerns that existed prior to the pandemic, you may show differences in coping behaviors. All of our individual traits play a part in our interpersonal health. Knowing yourself more deeply regarding your interpersonal branch of health will assist you in becoming discerning and intentional for how you interact with others; this awareness will improve the quality and richness of your interpersonal branch of health.

Quality vs. Quantity of Conscious Connections

Truth is, people will never recognize what has changed within you,
what makes you tick, what sets your heart and soul on fire,
or what causes a rage within your bloodstream,
unless they yearn to understand your soul.
–Kristin Michelle Elizabeth

Regardless of whether you need a few or many relationships in your life, the quality of these relationships—the ability for you to share not just human-to-human, but soul-to-soul—always makes the difference for the vitality of your interpersonal branch of health. Many models exist to educate us about how to create healthy relationships. To me, six main qualities help to create optimal interpersonal health: healthy communication, good boundaries, intact integrity, equality between those involved, mutual respect and unconditional appreciation.

Just as the Soul Health Model emphasizes that you need all branches to have reasonable health to create vitality for the entirety of the tree, the six interpersonal qualities of healthy relationships all work together to create a fully enriched interpersonal branch of health. Even if just one quality is lacking within a relationship, that connection will inevitably suffer. For example, it is impossible to have good boundaries with someone if they don't respect you. Your integrity will be compromised if you don't experience unconditionality from a loved one or partner. All qualities work together to enhance a relationship.

Below, each quality is described briefly:

Communication: Conscious relationships require this type of communication. Conscious communicators engage openly, honestly, clearly and with intention to enhance and/or maintain a relationship or group of relationships present in your social branch of health.

Boundaries: Personal boundaries are a sign of knowing your own limits or those of another. Holding healthy boundaries with others indicates a dedication to respecting both your own and your loved one's limits related to the ten branches of health.

Integrity: Having integrity means you are living life from the inside out—meaning that you know your inner self—your soul—enough to stand for what you need or don't need in your life to maintain optimal balance and health. This is perhaps the hardest quality to maintain when you are in a relationship that dims your light.

Equality: This quality reflects directly on whether your connection with someone is equally mutually life-affirming. An equal give and take nature to the relationship ensures that the connection is balanced.

Respect: Without respect for yourself, no other branch on your tree of life will be healthy. Also, if you wish to be respected by others, you have to respect yourself. Personal respect reflects your ability to uphold self-worth as well as accepting yourself wherever you are at any given time on your path.

Unconditionality: It seems we are taught to be critical of ourselves and others from a very young age. But placing conditions on ourselves or others disrupts our ability to have strong bonds. At our core, everyone wants to be understood, accepted and loved, but very few people fully accept themselves enough to accept others.

Take a few minutes to complete the following questionnaire to explore your interpersonal branch of health. Given the impact of the pandemic, it is likely that some areas have changed from pre-pandemic to now.

Questionnaire for the Interpersonal Branch of Health

On a scale of 1 to 10, rate the level of your health within each area described. A 10 describes optimal, radiant health, while a 1 describes an almost complete lack of health within the given aspect of the interpersonal branch. Remember, this questionnaire is designed to create a roadmap to overall radiant health. It is not meant to overwhelm you.

Communication
1._____I communicate well with the people in my life and they would agree.
2._____I communicate my feelings and needs well to those in my life.
3._____I am able to talk about difficult things with those in my life.
4._____I consider my friends and family to be good communicators.
5._____I limit the time I spend with people who don't communicate well.

Boundaries
1._____I know what healthy boundaries are.
2._____I have good physical and emotional boundaries with people in my life.
3._____I respect other people's boundaries.
4._____I can say no to others when I need to.
5._____I know when a personal boundary has been breached and I actively reestablish it.
6._____I avoid people who don't have good boundaries.
7._____I feel emotionally and physically safe with the people in my life.

Personal Integrity
1._____I know what personal integrity is.
2._____I only do things that feel right to me.
3._____I work to maintain the integrity of my relationships with others.
4._____I maintain my own personal integrity despite what others may say or do.
5._____I only spend time with those who respect my personal integrity.

Equality
1._____I know what equal partnership means.
2._____Friends, family, and my partner see me as an equal and treat me accordingly.
3._____I see and treat my friends, family, and partner as equals.
4._____My relationships with others are equally life-giving.

Respect
1._____My actions show that I respect myself completely.
2._____I feel completely respected by those in my life and I respect them completely.
3._____I feel respected by the people in my life even though they may not like what I say or do.
4._____I respect the people in my life even though I may not like what they say or do.

Unconditionality
1._____I know what it means to be unconditional toward myself and others.
2._____I unconditionally love and accept myself.
3._____I unconditionally accept my friends, family, and partner.
4._____Friends, family, and my partner unconditionally accept me.
5._____I see my own and others' judgments as cues to become more unconditional in some way.
6._____I can remain unconditional toward others even if they judge, hurt, or offend me.

As you rated the level of interpersonal health on the questionnaire, you likely identified relationships in your life that shifted during the pandemic. Some need adjustment in order to create healthier and more fulfilling interactions with others, while you might also find that some need to be minimized or eliminated altogether. It can help to consider the relationships in question by applying the Three Questions of Discernment: 1) "Is it meaningful?" 2) "Is it necessary?" and 3) "Does it feed my soul?" It might also be helpful to explore the quality of the relationships according to the three main characteristics of conscious relationships—*connectivity* (Do you share valuable interests?), *intentionality* (Are your interactions thoughtful and purposive?) and *explicit reality* (Can you say your interactions are fully and clearly expressive?).

Your Vulnerable But Authentic Truth

We are at our most powerful the moment
we no longer need to be powerful.
—Eric Micha'el Leventhal

Although the word "vulnerability" didn't directly come up in dialogue with the healthcare workers I interviewed, many did allude to feeling extremely defenseless and exposed both early in the pandemic and in the many months that followed. Most healthcare practitioners wouldn't agree with the quote by Eric Micha'el Leventhal noted above since they are taught and expected to know the answers with certainty and to never be wrong. With the way the pandemic arrived and then unfolded, there is no way healthcare providers could have remained confident in their trained roles, let alone in any of their relationships when their defenses came down. For many, forced vulnerability likely impacted their relationships—for better or worse—more than any other factor related to the global health crisis. When you think about the six interpersonal qualities of healthy relationships (communication, boundaries, personal integrity, equality, respect and unconditionality), each requires a partner, loved ones, friends or coworkers who can receive and accept the vulnerability shown by a healthcare practitioner in order to keep your relationships intact. If you, as a healthcare provider, did not feel you could be vulnerable in this situation, it is inevitable that not only did your social and interpersonal branches of health suffer, so did your overall tree of health.

The Cunningham Group, a medical malpractice insurance company, published an article about vulnerability, shame and healthcare in 2015. Three main areas of perceived weakness by providers were discussed: the admission that a provider didn't know the answer to something, knowing how to talk to a patient and family members about end-of-life care, and the occurrence of a medical mistake. No one would be surprised that nearly every healthcare provider I interviewed said they experienced each of these situations during COVID-19. If this is the case and you didn't feel comfortable talking with those in your social branch of health, many unseen wounds will remain if vulnerability isn't addressed along your path to healing.

Many studies show how distressing and shameful these experiences can be for providers. In general, physicians are shown to already have higher levels of suicidal ideation than the general public. Because practitioners don't often sense they can discuss their feelings related to such events, ideation can be even higher following a recent medical error—something that was inevitable in the early phases of the pandemic. One study showed that surgeons have up to three times higher frequency of suicidal thoughts in general than the communities they serve and that 16.2% experience these thoughts following disclosure of a medical error. Although no studies have yet been published regarding shame and vulnerability related to the care provided during the pandemic, it is certain that many providers suffered from not knowing how to help their patients or even how to protect their loved ones.

As a psychologist, I am well aware of the need to share and "process" my stress with colleagues and those in my immediate social circle, but given the pressure for healthcare providers to perform perfectly and not share their vulnerabilities with others, it is possible and even likely that many suffered in silence. This likely caused even more of a strain on interpersonal relationships, particularly if a partner didn't display unconditional, respectful communication and support.

Vulnerability researcher and expert, Brené Brown, says, "Owning our story can be hard but not nearly as difficult as spending our lives running from it. Embracing our vulnerabilities is risky but not nearly as dangerous as giving up on love and belonging and joy—the experiences that make us the most vulnerable. Only when we are brave enough to explore the darkness will we discover the infinite power of our light." She emphasizes that vulnerability is not a negative thing—it actually builds both personal strength and the relationships upon which we rely for support. To Brown, personal sharing can help to enrich and bolster relationships if individuals are open and available to one another.

When it comes to soul-to-soul relationships, vulnerability is the cornerstone of strength and bonding. When it comes to healing, sharing the challenges of your inner self *is* the only way to heal the wounds that most deeply affect the essence of who you are. Whether we like it or not, allowing ourselves to be vulnerable is necessary to fully embrace our path to healing.

A nursing home director whom I invited to interview for this book initially said he was too raw to talk about his experience. He went on to say that no one wanted to hear a front line account of what he went through. Once I told him that's what I needed to hear in order to help others, it brought tears and he opened up to share more about his experience. He witnessed incredible loneliness and death among the patients and related extreme worry for his employees. Other directors suggested I speak with their nursing staff instead, clearly deferring the option in order to protect themselves from opening the wounds.

As I mentioned in a previous chapter, it seemed like requests to be interviewed for this book served as an opening and outlet for many providers. Granted, I *am* a psychologist and I know how to listen. But I also care deeply about the painful experiences that impact a person's life. If you are a healthcare worker who wants those in your life to more fully understand what you need from an interpersonal perspective, I'd encourage you to share this chapter with those you care for and love. Perhaps this will provide an opening to rebuild and/or enhance your relationships as well.

Should I Stay or Should I Go?

For there is power, which, as it is in you, is in him also, and could therefore very well bring you together, if it were for the best.
—Ralph Waldo Emerson

Many question whether it is time to let go of a connection, sometimes one that has been a part of your life for a very long time. You can ask yourself the *Three Questions of Discernment*, explore the six qualities of healthy relationships and revisit the questionnaires in both this chapter and the previous one related to social health. All will help you determine how your relationships affect your overall health. However, I want to offer you a metaphor that might help you determine whether you should stay in or leave a relationship. Keep in mind that when we are in our darkest days, nothing seems bright—even a relationship that once illuminated every aspect of your tree. After working on your other branches of health, you might be able to salvage a relationship and reconnect in a way that brings you to a higher level of health.

After over three decades working in mental health, I have formed a metaphor for pretty much everything. Because much of my work is both "whole health" and spiritual in nature, I often bring the bigger picture into view for those I serve. I have watched relationships of my own come and go—romantic partnerships, friendships, family connections, collegial contacts and simple acquaintances. I now know that when my soul's path crosses another's, it happens so I can learn. Each relationship, including the way it starts and ends, happens for a reason. I often say that love is laced with lessons—regardless of whichever type of connection we make. I also say that love serves as a lure—a "shiny object" that creates an opportunity to learn. As Ralph Waldo Emerson wrote in his quote above about the power of two souls being drawn together, there is also power and mystery of how and why we meet.

I talk to clients, workshop participants and now you—healthcare providers—about what I call the "magnet metaphor". There seems to be a "divine design" that takes place between two souls. The Universe (God, Spirit, whatever you want to call the highest power you believe exists) creates a magnetic energy that draws light sources together—in this case those light sources are souls. With each magnetic draw, the souls involved are supposed to learn and grow in some way through their contact, but can't do so without the experience of one another. This applies to any relationship we have in our lives, including with family members. Even a chance passing of souls can provide an opportunity to absorb a profound lesson depending on the circumstances. Many of you likely experienced this with patients you treated prior, during or after the pandemic.

I go on to tell people that sometimes one or both of the magnets begins to "flip" through the experience of conflict, disappointment or other things that create separation between the poles. As humans, we try to put the magnets back in alignment so we can re-establish a bond. Sometimes this is done through intentional healthy actions and sometimes we try haphazardly in order to avoid loss. This can go on for years and even decades, which can actually add even more distance between the connection instead of just admitting it is time to go your separate ways. This "flipping" is undoubtedly part of the evolutionary process for one or both souls IF they become aware of what they are supposed to learn. Otherwise, it can just be pure hell.

Sometimes you learn that you can't just flip the magnets back into place to reconnect and the magnets repel each other away in opposite directions. In some cases the experience of being repelled causes a growth spurt that was necessary to learn something that could bring the souls even closer together. For example, I tell clients that affairs can either make or break a romantic relationship if both individuals within the relationship are willing to explore the dynamics that pulled them apart. This can sometimes repair the disconnection and bond two souls even more deeply together.

In my experience, both personally and in observing clients, the bigger and faster the attraction to someone, the larger the lessons that can be learned. Also, this magnet metaphor can apply to non-romantic relationships. Often in family relations, we don't seemingly "choose" the souls that enter our lives—they are already part of our social "soul" group. But we can still experience the sense of being repelled from these connections if we recognize that they are not healthy for us. The same is true for friendships, collegial contacts and any other relationship we may have formed. In essence, each relationship provides the opportunity for us to learn. Each also offers the chance to understand ourselves so we can more closely and intentionally practice the *Three Questions of Discernment* as well as assess our relationships based on the six qualities of healthy relationships mentioned before. Every relationship and connection that occurs in our lives assists us in getting to know ourselves better. It is what we do with the knowledge that makes the difference for our overall soul health.

No doubt, in reading about this metaphor, you've already examined multiple relationships in your life. The awareness of how we are drawn to or repelled from other souls might help you to determine which dynamics between you and others might need work. It might also help you decide if it is time to stay in or leave a relationship.

The Evolution of Self and Relationship

Whatever relationships you have attracted into your life at this moment, are precisely the ones you need in your life at this moment. There is hidden meaning behind all events, and this hidden meaning is serving your own evolution.
—Deepak Chopra

Our relationships with others make us who we are. But one thing I've learned is that instead of learning to love someone else more, the main purpose of our connections is to teach us to love ourselves. This illuminates what we need and don't need in order to lead our most radiant life. It is self-love that allows us to live our best lives and this is what healing the wounded aspects of the human condition is about. We cannot experience true health unless we know our souls deeply and create a life that is fully aligned with its needs and desires. This is a process, which is why I so often use the word evolution to describe the healing path.

The health of our interpersonal branch of health is dependent on how we interact with others, which might have changed since the beginning of the pandemic. When it feels right, take another look at the questions for the Questionnaire for the Interpersonal Branch of Health so you can use the E.V.O.L.V.E. protocol to improve the health of this branch.

E–Examine

- In what ways have your patterns of interacting with others changed?
- What factors have you become aware of that need attention (trust, safety, shared or divergent values)?
- How has the meaning of relationships changed since the beginning of the pandemic?
- Have certain "magnets" flipped since the pandemic began?

V–Vision

+ How do you see your interactive style changing as you work on your interpersonal branch of health?
+ What do you see improving as a result of working on your interpersonal health?

O–Observe

+ How have your interactions with others become more or less *meaningful*?
+ What do you now know is *necessary* for you to have a healthy interpersonal branch of health?
+ Do the behaviors of those in your life *feed your soul*?

L–Learn

+ What do you need to work on in order to enjoy better interpersonal health? (Boundaries, Respect, Communication, Self-Esteem, Equality, Unconditionality?)
+ What have you learned about healthy relationships since the beginning of the pandemic?
+ What have you learned about unhealthy relationships since the beginning of the pandemic?

V–Venture

+ How would you like to address new interactive styles with others?
+ How do you envision yourself with others in the future?
+ When you see your interpersonal future, what has changed?

E–Elevate

+ How can you elevate your interpersonal health to something more fulfilling?
+ What new mindset can you adopt in order to brighten your interpersonal branch of health?

CHAPTER ELEVEN

THE INTELLECTUAL/OCCUPATIONAL BRANCH OF HEALTH
The Soul's Mission

Every person has a longing to be significant; to make a contribution;
to be a part of something noble and purposeful.
–JOHN MAXWELL

No one expected to be part of a pandemic, but healthcare workers undoubtedly played a bigger role than any other professionals in how this global event unfolded. This reality added even more pressure to a field that was already responsible for most life and death decisions, including their own. An eye surgeon I spoke with noted that it was the first time in her career she and her friends and colleagues questioned whether they wanted to die for their jobs. All of them decided their dedication to their work was worth the risk.

John Maxwell, one of my favorite leadership authors and speakers, wrote a book called *The Journey from Success to Significance*. In it, he explains that finding success is the easy part of professional development, adding that it is when you strive for significance that you most leave your comfort zone. When I think about the over one hundred conversations I had with healthcare workers across the United States and Canada, there is no doubt that COVID-19 had stretched all the practitioners' professional edges. What remained noble and awe-inspiring is that each provider continued their mission to help—they just wanted to make a difference. No matter how difficult their experience, they still wanted to do their part. There is nothing more significant than that.

While some consciously choose healthcare as their profession, many are *called* to enter lines of work that allow them to help others heal. Either path of deciding on a career must align with a person's deep essence in order to create a healthy intellectual/occupational branch of health. William Osler, one of the co-founders of Johns Hopkins Hospital said, "The practice of medicine is an art, not a trade; a calling, not a business; a calling in which your heart will be exercised equally with your head." A calling—or inner stirring toward your aligned path—helps you identify and create your life mission, one that brings passion and meaning to both your own existence and to those you serve. As long as we align our intellectual/occupational branch of health, our chosen career path will always go from success to significance.

Maxwell wrote about five fundamental differences between those who strive for success vs. significance: motives, influence, time, focus and reward.

Motives—As a young pastor, he started out asking himself what his congregation could do to help him learn. As he matured, his motive changed from, "What can I do to help them?" to "What can I do to help others, so they go on to help those around them?"

Influence—He also realized that with success, his influence was limited. But when he shifted to offering something significant, his influence was limitless.

Time—He came to know that although success can last a lifetime, significance could be passed on for several generations.

Focus—His focus changed from "How can I add value to myself?" to "How can I add value to others?" He changed his view to the significance he could bring to others, for the sake of the people around those others.

Reward—The reward of his work went from his own joy as a result of his success to his joy resulting from another's success instead. He found it much more productive and satisfying to get beyond himself to help people grow and develop.

Many of the healthcare workers I interviewed reported that both their approach to work and their sense of significance deepened during the pandemic. Early in 2021, I spoke with a public health nurse who went from school nursing to working in the county health COVID clinic. She said she wanted to do what she could to participate in changing outcomes during the pandemic. Many other healthcare professionals left "safer" jobs to join frontline staff to do what they could. Several of the travel nurses I spoke with felt a call to assist in the hardest hit parts of the country. They uprooted everything to jump in and help. A second-year medical student said that because she wasn't yet able to help patients directly, she spent all of her extra time early in the health crisis assembling masks for the medical staff needing them. A friend of mine who is a vice president at a local medical system spent the early part of the pandemic going from store to store to purchase trash cans, plastic bags and anything else she could fit in her car to help supply what couldn't be ordered.

Because healthcare workers began working long hours even when their children were sent home from school, students from the local medical school (including medical, nursing, physician assistant and others) volunteered to babysit and mentor their faculty's children so they could continue to serve those in need. Along with taking on many extra clients and extending my own hours, I made a weekly drop at a nearby food pantry since so many were out of work and couldn't afford even the basic foods. No one I spoke to wanted to score points; helpers just naturally want to help.

Maxwell also said, "An intentional life embraces only the things that will add to the mission of significance." In his own professional growth, he realized there was much more to intellectual and occupational health than success. It is when we want to make a difference that we experience the most fulfillment. With soul health in mind, it is when we intentionally align our life mission with our inner needs that we and others are brought the most light.

The Decision to Stay in Healthcare or Go Beyond

It is more reasonable than ever to assume that many healthcare providers will evaluate whether they want to continue in their chosen field, the career to which they were called. Many of them did just that when it came to deciding whether or not to get a vaccine. When it comes to our soul's evolution, the human condition often alters what we think will be a straight path. Often, the detours life presents allow us to more deeply consider if there is something we need to adjust or realign to create an even better fit to our branches of health. Remember, it is often our discomfort that initiates change, so perhaps your healing path will include a newly paved road.

As you will see in the Questionnaire for the Intellectual/Occupational Branch of Health, I've outlined six primary concepts to consider in aligning this branch for optimal living: mental stimulation, curiosity and passion, thought processes, sense of control, responsibilities and openness to change. As you read more, consider your ideas about each concept to assess whether your chosen field within healthcare remains the best fit. Keep in mind, this may have changed with your experience of the pandemic.

Questionnaire for the Intellectual/Occupational Branch of Health

On a scale of 1 to 10, rate the level of your health within each area described. A 10 describes optimal, radiant health, while a 1 describes an almost complete lack of health within the given aspect of the intellectual/ occupation branch. Remember, this questionnaire is designed to create a roadmap to overall radiant health. It is not meant to overwhelm you.

Mental Stimulation
1._____I feel mentally challenged by the activities in my work and home life.
2._____My life is mentally stimulating and interesting.
3._____Generally, I do not feel bored.
4._____I actively use my creativity in my life.
5._____I engage in activities that keep my thoughts and memory sharp.

Curiosity and Passion
1._____I am excited about my life.
2._____I am naturally curious about how things work.
3._____I actively pursue things I'm passionate about.
4._____I am constantly trying to learn new things.
5._____I feel satisfied with the activities in my life.
6._____I am personally invested in everything I do.

Thought Processes
1._____I easily maintain my train of thought.
2._____I am a good problem solver.
3._____My memory is sharp.
4._____Generally, I can remember what I have recently read.
5._____I have clear, un-muddled thoughts.
6._____I make decisions easily.

Sense of Control
1._____I have a sense of control in intellectual tasks.
2._____I have control in my work environment.
3._____I can negotiate with others in my work environment to meet mutual needs.
4._____Changes at work are discussed openly.
5._____People in my work environment value my opinion.

Responsibilities
1._____My daily responsibilities are reasonable.
2._____I feel good about what I accomplish.
3._____I can easily accomplish my responsibilities.
4._____I rarely feel overwhelmed.

Openness to Change
1._____I am open to change.
2._____I adapt well to change.
3._____I don't take changes made by others personally.
4._____I see change as a new challenge.
5._____I believe that periodic change can benefit me in some way.

Mental Stimulation

For many, mental stimulation is food for the soul. The process of learning something new can be meaningful and necessary as well. Without something to exercise our brains, we would become bored and our inner self would feel malnourished. Simply stated, without mental stimulation we could not evolve. While many healthcare workers enjoy feeling challenged on the job, too much stimulation can lead to overwhelm and burnout.

Curiosity and Passion

While curiosity is the desire to learn and to *know*, having a passion for something provides unlimited enthusiasm or a strong liking for something. Both are essential to intellectual/occupational health. The more curious an employee, the more adaptable they tend to be in new situations. They are also more likely to report job satisfaction and perform at high levels while on the job. An uninterested or passionless soul struggles to thrive; its light becomes dim. Several of the healthcare workers I interviewed said their passion for work continued, and once over the initial shock of the course of disease, many noted that the opportunity to learn about COVID-19 renewed their curiosity for learning how to help others. But there's a difference between a desire to learn and an imposed crash course about an unexpected global health event.

Thought Processing

Focus—the ability to stay on task—is key to intellectual/occupational health. Our soul health is directly impacted by many factors of the human condition including stress, depression, anxiety, sleeplessness, overwhelm, distractibility, illness, structural changes in the brain, chemical dependency and others. Other misaligned branches of your tree of life, such as relationship issues, can also negatively impact the ability to process information. When our thoughts become foggy, our inner light can also become foggy. All of the healthcare workers interviewed for this book reported some form of alteration to thought processing, mostly related to overwhelm and stress.

Sense of Control

Job satisfaction is closely tied with how much control an employee feels they have at work. Sudden shifts in work load, tasks, number of hours worked, coworkers, health risk, training opportunities, or inadequate training all contribute to low sense of control in a work environment. Needless to say, all of these factors may have changed for healthcare workers depending on their specific role played during the pandemic, adding to a marked lack of control.

Responsibilities

It is hard to feel fulfilled when you have too much to do and you aren't doing work you were hired to do. When an employee doesn't feel sufficiently trained to perform a task, it can significantly disrupt a sense of both balance and job satisfaction. An overwhelmed human inevitably leads to an overwhelmed soul, thus making a healthcare worker involved in caring for others during a pandemic susceptible to a misaligned intellectual/occupational branch of health.

Openness to Change

Because change is a given part of any job, openness to adjust to new ideas and tasks can help to maintain intellectual/occupational health. Openness to change equals readiness to evolve, whereas resistance to adjust blocks or inhibits our growth. Incidentally, the need to change something often releases us from feeling stuck—imposed change can dislodge our soul from the sense that we have no options. The pandemic changed nearly everything we knew about how to care for ourselves and others—not to mention function in general—and forced us to advance beyond our previously familiar path.

Unknowingly, throughout the pandemic, many healthcare workers were challenged within each of these six areas of intellectual/

occupational health. As you explore this branch as part of your path to healing, consider whether your current career choice meets the criteria for meaning, necessity and the ability to feed your soul.

Also, take some time to complete the Questionnaire for Intellectual/ Occupational Health to more directly assess what might need to be considered or adjusted. This will help you decide whether your chosen field or the area of healthcare in which you were *called* to serve is still aligned with the essence of who you are and what will fulfill you in the years to come.

While some have already left careers in healthcare, many will likely adjust their intellectual/occupational branch of health to better fit their developing tree. It is possible that your experience working during the pandemic will change how you approach this important branch of health.

The Imposter Dilemma

"The exaggerated esteem in which my lifework is held makes me very ill at ease. I feel compelled to think of myself as an involuntary swindler."
—Albert Einstein

It's hard to believe that the iconic genius, Albert Einstein, believed he was an imposter given all of his immeasurably significant contributions and the influence he holds throughout the world. Many of those I interviewed for this book mentioned feeling similar, especially early in the pandemic. Providers from nearly every medical profession and level of care mentioned they felt like a fraud.

Published just before the pandemic arrived in the United States, an article about imposter syndrome presented the sweeping statistic that nearly 82% of professionals experience this intellectual "condition". This syndrome is considered a prevalent behavioral health condition that both impairs performance and contributes to burnout. The pattern of symptoms generally includes self-doubt, apprehension, ambivalence and insecurity about competence and knowledge—all of which were reported by the healthcare workers interviewed for this book.

Given the urgency to "get things right" at the beginning of the pandemic, all healthcare professionals were challenged with the pattern of symptoms related to feeling like a fraud. A surgeon I interviewed admitted that although he felt his surgical skills remained sharp, he was completely disarmed on the subject of knowing how to protect patients, himself and his team during procedures early in the health crisis. A psychologist in private practice located in a hard-hit urban area often said to herself, "I'm trying to help you, but I'm not doing so well, myself." Throughout interviews, I heard words like "humbled" and "humility" as professionals tried to make sense of how their certainty had been shaken.

Feeling valued is essential to intellectual/occupational health, but when we feel incapable of offering something significant to others, our inner light is often dimmed. The challenge is that helpers rarely feel they are helping enough. Employee impact expert, Tom Rath said, "The single biggest threat to our wellbeing tends to be ourselves." He also said, "When we build on our strengths and daily successes—instead of focusing on failures—we simply learn more." But when it comes to how a health professional feels about their performance during a pandemic, you can bet they focus on the mistakes they made more than their successes. Significance is lost and the intellectual branch of health can break and wither.

When a dedicated professional starts questioning her or his career, you can bet that a full exploration of their tree of life makes sense. The pandemic will always be seen as a life-altering event—a detour from an already challenging human condition. But with evolution in mind, it may be helpful to consider the ways the events have made you even better. Rath noted, "You cannot be anything you want to be—but you can be a lot more of who you already are." That's the spirit of evolution. If we allow ourselves to grow, our expansion is infinite.

Explore how you can enhance your intellectual/occupational branch of health using the E.V.O.L.V.E. protocol:

E–Examine

+ How has your overall intellectual/occupational health changed?
+ What needs to change in order to improve this branch of health now?

V–Vision

+ When you envision your intellectual/occupational health in the future, what is different?
+ What changes do you envision to enhance this branch of health?

O–Observe

+ How has your interest in your occupation changed since the start of the pandemic?
+ How have your thoughts overall changed?
+ Is there anything you now know about yourself that you didn't know before?

L–Learn

+ What have you learned about yourself with regard to your intellectual/occupational health?
+ What have you learned about what you need and don't need to have more fulfillment in your work?
+ What can you learn about what you need out of a work environment in order to thrive?

V–Venture

+ Do you need to try something new? Go back to school? Find a new place to work?
+ What would you like to do to "stretch your edges" in your intellectual/occupational health?
+ What is the first step to moving into your new vision?

E–Elevate

+ What do you need to do to elevate your future?
+ What will help you overcome concerns about "stepping up"?
+ Who will assist you in moving into an elevated future?

CHAPTER TWELVE
THE ENVIRONMENTAL BRANCH OF HEALTH
Your Tree's House and Home

The state of our surroundings tells the conditions of our soul.
—LAILAH GIFTY AKITA

Never before has the healthcare environment posed so much danger—not on actual battlefields, but with a more invasive enemy, one that is unseen, sneaky and lethal. Places of healing were previously considered safe havens from potential harm. But for the first time, no one, including many healthcare providers, wanted to enter these danger zones. Couple a dangerous work environment with extreme precautions that were of necessity instituted at home and in every other aspect of our surroundings, it is inevitable that our overall health diminished.

As author Lailah Gifty Akita asserted, the state of the world around us is a good measure for the conditions of the world within us. Given the multiple layers of impact on our environmental branch of health, our souls, no doubt suffered as COVID-19 invaded our surroundings.

With regard to soul health, the environmental branch of health also emphasizes the relationship with our immediate, global and universal surroundings. It also acknowledges our internal world as well—the

150

"atmosphere" of our soul. Because our outside environment often reflects how we feel inside—and vice versa, we must pay attention to both our internal and external situations in order to create and maintain a healthy environmental branch of health. Of course, this branch also pertains to things like safety and security as well as how orderly, clean and functional it is.

In the Questionnaire for the Environmental Branch of Health, you will find five main components: "Healthy Hearth", Aesthetics, Ecological Impact, Sacred Surroundings and Cultural and Emotional Environment. From my interviews with healthcare providers for this book, none of these areas were left untouched by the pandemic. They will be briefly described here:

Healthy Hearth

Prior to the arrival of COVID-19, many took for granted their access to food and water, shelter, general safely, comfortable climate, minimal exposure to pollutants or other dangerous agents and general cleanliness and order. The pandemic changed all of this, both at work and at home as no environment felt secure. What was once relatively safe became a focus of suspicion and fear that the unseen intruder was looming.

Aesthetics

The "aesthetics" of our environment usually feeds our souls most. During the pandemic, many households and workplaces suddenly became much more sterile and far less appealing. Both work and home added protective features including specialized equipment, sterilizing supplies, baskets or barrels for "contaminated" clothing, "decontamination zones" and more. What creates a health-supportive environment depends on the individual needs of the beholder's soul; unfortunately, often this differed between domestic partners, family members and children, which added further stress to an already stressful situation.

Ecological Impact

During the pandemic, our awareness about ecological impact pretty much went out the window as healthcare providers simply did whatever they could to get through each day. While this aspect of the environmental branch of health usually pertains to our relationship with our planet, our attention shifted to the global health impact the virus had on the world around us. When the world shut down, we did see an almost immediate improvement in the health of the planet itself—less pollution with fewer cars on the road, less trash on highways and streets since people were required to stay at home and less ocean creatures disrupted because cruise ships and other seaward vehicles were docked. But we also saw cardboard from delivery boxes stack up, clutter from uncontrolled retail therapy, more plastic bags since most stores halted use of personal bags and more glass and cans in the trash or recycling bins due to increased alcohol sales.

Sacred Surroundings

Soul health emphasizes the need to create and maintain the world around us as a sacred surrounding, an environment conducive to staying grounded, "fed" and at peace. This could include the addition of things like spaces for reflection and meditation, the inclusion of candles, aromatherapy and fountains or simply setting an intention that the space you keep will provide a warm, calming and restorative backdrop to day-to-day living. However, there was nothing sacred about COVID-19 and few were able to maintain a spiritual practice, let alone set the intention for keeping either their work or home environments "well lit"—bright in the midst of the inherent emotional darkness.

Cultural and "Emotional" Environments

Our environment doesn't define us, but it does influence us, particularly if it is not well suited for our soul's health. We must become aware of how well our surroundings affirm and assist us in our soul's evolution.

Along with the pandemic came much cultural strife due to the thick layer of racial discord that was present at the same time. Culturally, this created an even deeper wound for many healthcare workers as many noted during interviews that many events stirred more disharmony than the virus created alone.

Another environmental aspect of health that warrants attention is the emotional environment in which we live. Numerous healthcare workers noted during interviews that stress and tension escalated at home. Several changed their physical environments to cope with the festering emotional surroundings, moving out of homes when relationships were disrupted. Others noted increased tension in spending far more time with family members in small spaces as everyone either worked or performed schooling responsibilities from home. As a psychologist, I believe the emotional environment of home, work and community as well as global environments can raise disturbing emotions, all of which can have a detrimental impact on our overall health.

The following questionnaire can provide a brief look at your environmental branch of health. Clearly, the health of our surroundings requires more than an appealing view. In reviewing the items, consider more carefully how "soul supportive" your environment currently is. This will give you an idea of what needs attention or adjustment to attain overall health.

Questionnaire for the Environmental Branch of Health

On a scale of 1 to 10, rate the level of your health within each area described. A 10 describes optimal, radiant health, while a 1 describes an almost complete lack of health within the given aspect of the environmental branch. Remember, this questionnaire is designed to create a roadmap to overall radiant health. It is not meant to overwhelm you.

Healthy Hearth
1._____I live in clean, safe, and healthy surroundings.
2._____I like where I live (my neighborhood, state, country, and climate).
3._____I live and work in clutter-free environments.
4._____I take care of my personal environment.
5._____I practice regular home maintenance and safety measures (change filters, check for leaks, etc.).
6._____My home provides good shelter (is insulated, free of drafts, leaks, etc.).
7._____I work to reduce pollution in my environment (air, chemical, noise, etc.).

Aesthetics
1._____My personal surroundings fit who I am.
2._____My work surroundings fit who I am.
3._____I take pleasure in what I place in my surroundings.
4._____I know what I need around me to feel safe, comfortable, and fulfilled.
5._____I actively rid myself of things that don't fit my preferences.
6._____I look forward to spending time in my surroundings.

Ecological Impact
1._____I understand that how I choose to live affects the environment in which I live.
2._____I do not waste food, water, energy, or fuel.
3._____I buy and keep only what I need.
4._____I only purchase 'eco-friendly' products (appliances, cleaning products, compostable packaging, etc.).
5._____I am conscious of minimizing my impact on the environment.
6._____I do not litter and always clean up after myself and those I'm responsible for (family, pets. etc.).
7._____I avoid using toxic and/or harmful chemicals (cleaning products, pesticides, herbicides, etc.).

Sacred Surroundings
1._____I feel connected with the earth.
2._____I feel connected with my personal environment.
3._____I actively work to make my environment peaceful and calming.
4._____My surroundings reflect my core beliefs.
5._____I know when I need to reconnect with the earth and with my personal surroundings.
6._____I spend time outside to connect with the earth.

Cultural and Emotional Environment
1._____I live in a place that fits my cultural beliefs and values.
2._____I work in an environment that fits my cultural beliefs and values.
3._____My personal environment is calm and free of tension.
4._____My work environment is calm and free of tension.
5._____I live in a trusting environment.
6._____I work in a trusting environment.
7._____I feel accepted at home and at work.
8._____I feel emotionally safe in my environment.

As a healthcare provider, you are likely more aware than ever that the environmental branch of health goes far beyond the air we breathe and the land on which we walk. In order to attain soul health, we need to assess how well we fit into different aspects of our environment (home, work, the part of the country or world in which we reside, what helps us to feel grounded), and what we need in order for our souls to survive and thrive. Our willingness to address these needs is essential in creating a vigorous environmental branch of health as well as the health of our inner self.

Intrusions of Personal Space

Be careful of who and what you let into your space.
Not everyone is worthy of your presence.
–Ledisi, R&B Artist

Our personal space is part of our environment. While the pandemic eliminated the possibility of interaction with friends and loved ones, it also created an intrusion on personal space—both with the body, itself and often with living in close quarters with others. For many healthcare practitioners I interviewed, this created a major issue in overall health.

Several healthcare providers mentioned during interviews that they became both exhausted and resentful of PPE, despite its protective nature. Many personalized their experience of gowning and masking up, feeling like the process was not only a personal affront but also an obstacle to the pace of work they were accustomed to performing. Many suffered from face sores due to wearing masks for multiple hours a day or simply felt the gear placed unwanted boundaries between themselves, patients, coworkers and loved ones. Numerous providers noted they began to feel uncomfortable when others stood too close whether on the job or not. Some providers said they felt confident in their ability to protect others, but loved ones were scared to have close contact with them causing a rift in relationships, marriages and other family dynamics.

Whether an individual was an introvert or extrovert, COVID-19 created challenges for sharing space with others. Because the pandemic shut down both schools and businesses, many healthcare providers suddenly found themselves spending too much time in the company of people—sometimes in very small spaces. If issues were present prior to the pandemic, they often became magnified and worsened throughout it. Even when conflict was rare or non-existent, it often emerged because tensions became too high to manage.

While interviewing a psychologist in a large metropolitan area, I noticed how small the room was in which he was completing the Zoom call. He admitted that his stress had greatly increased once he moved his practice home, not only because his wife and children were also sharing the space, but also because the space was rather small to begin with. He added that he hadn't noticed prior to everyone being at home for so long. Several providers mentioned they separated or divorced spouses during the pandemic because they found they couldn't spend time together in close quarters under such stressful circumstances. Despite feelings of isolation, several still chose to leave relationships to maintain their overall mental health.

Many healthcare providers also mentioned that the emotional environment of their workplaces worsened greatly during the pandemic. Numerous practitioners experienced the divide between healthcare staff and administrators widening as a result of not feeling valued during the outbreak. Others felt the discord between coworkers due to burnout, and stress darkened the energy of their workplaces—saying they dreaded interacting with coworkers more than with their dying patients. Some expressed sadness about the loss of once close collegial connections.

Arron Wood, an Australian environmentalist said, "With a healthy environment all our lives are enriched – without it our lives are diminished. The environment is and will always be number one – One Life, One World, Our Future." Although he made this statement about the actual state of the planet, it applies to the environmental branch of soul health as well. As mentioned in previous chapters, when something diminishes our light, we suffer. In this case, the emotional environment of home or work can have a direct impact on other branches of our tree of life, thus disrupting overall health in general.

Swedish doctor and psychiatrist, Axel Munthe said, "The soul needs more space than the body." As you explore your environmental branch of health, you might notice that you've changed with regard to how much time and space you need to experience full health.

Controlling Our Environment

There is a whole crazy world around you. You can't control it, so don't even try. Because the more you try to control the environment, the more it controls you.
—Frederick Lenz, Spiritual Author

What happens when the one thing that has always seemed constant gets completely out of control? We could once count on the simplest parts of our surroundings to bring us comfort—our homes, our offices, our beds—even our pillow. With COVID-19, for many even these "constants" changed. Continuity and consistency are often the factors that stabilize us when we feel the most unstable, but very little was left undisturbed with the many changes that came with the pandemic. As author, Frederick Lenz said, sometimes the more you try to control your surroundings, the less you feel you can control.

A local veterinarian told the funniest story I heard while interviewing healthcare workers for this book. Like many clinicians, she was suddenly forced to change everything about how she practiced her trade. While talking about how she coped during the pandemic, she shared a story about an attempt to control her home environment—the only thing she thought she had a hold on. This attempt completely backfired, but it did teach her something about herself.

Soon after the national shutdown, she started to focus on her house.

She said she spent days reorganizing her kitchen pantry until it felt like everything was in place—easy to find, tidy and accessible. She was proud of her work and very satisfied that the room was finally the way she wanted it after she and her family moved into the home a few years prior. She returned from work a few days later to find that her husband had completely dismantled her prideful project. He, too, was trying to manage something. For some reason, he had decided the pantry needed new shelving and without discussing it with his wife, he removed all of the items from the room and placed them in the dining room just a few steps away. She said she was so traumatized by his actions that she began to cry uncontrollably. She said, "The only thing I felt that I could control was completely gone." Although she loves her husband dearly, she admitted that it took several weeks to get past the violation. Even funnier, though, is that her husband admitted he had no idea why he decided to dismantle the pantry because he rarely cooked. They both just wanted something that was in their control to manage. They are still happily married and now have a funny "pandemic story" to share.

As she told the story, she and I had a good laugh. I could relate to her strife, mostly because I did the same thing as a young kid. I found myself organizing the family pantry "for fun" at times. I've always had good spatial skills and it just felt better to have most things in line. What I realized later was that I, too, was trying to control my environment because after my father's accident when I was nine years old, very little felt aligned. Early in the pandemic, I used my time to completely redesign and re-landscape my back yard, creating three new gardens, installing stone steps down the hill and spreading mulch over a very large space. Literally on the last day of the project, I tore the meniscus in my left knee and found myself nearly immobile for months. What I did to control my environment almost literally broke a different branch of my tree of life.

Both the physical and emotional environment around you affects your overall environmental health. As you explore the Questionnaire for the Environmental Branch of Health, consider how the E.V.O.L.V.E. protocol can help you improve this branch of health:

E–Examine

- What has changed for you in terms of your environmental branch of health?
- What do you need – or don't need—around you to create an overall healthy environmental branch of health?

V–Vision

- How do you envision your optimal environmental health to look in the future?
- How do you envision this new outlook will improve your overall soul health?

O–Observe

- What is *meaningful* about your environmental health? What is not? How will this influence what you change?
- What is *necessary* to keep as part of your environmental health? What is *necessary* to release?
- Do both your physical and emotional environments *feed your soul*? If not, what needs to change?

L–Learn

- What have you learned about yourself with regard to both physical and emotional aspects of your environmental branch of health?
- How would you like to learn more about what you need from both aspects of your environmental health?

V–Venture

- What will help you improve your environmental branch of health?
- How can you explore new ways of enhancing your environmental health?

E–Elevate

+ What would help you "elevate" both your physical and emotional environments?
+ What do you need to tell yourself as you step into a more satisfying environmental branch of health?
+ While many consider environmental health only as a material or physical aspect of the world around them, it is important to remember that the emotional component of our environment plays a key role in whether we experience overall soul health.

CHAPTER THIRTEEN

THE FINANCIAL BRANCH OF HEALTH

The Money Tree

Of all the things that human beings make and do for
each other, it is the unquantifiable ones that
contribute most to human happiness.

—CHARLES EISENTEIN

Financial matters threaten humanity more immediately than many—
or even all—of the other factors of the human condition. This is true
because not only do we need money to live, but also because modern
society has placed great importance on money as a sign of both success
and an ability to thrive. Author, Charles Eisenstein, emphasizes in his
work that finances affect society in a deep and pervasive way, but notes
that no amount of money can actually make a person fully secure or
happy. The Soul Health Model illustrates that one "healthy" branch
alone doesn't make for overall satisfaction and contentment.

Along with a direct threat to our physical health, the coronavirus
pandemic sent shockwaves through many healthcare providers' financial
branch of health. Early in 2020, large organizations cut some practitioner
salaries by as much as thirty-five percent. Some healthcare workers

were furloughed from their jobs or lost them altogether. One clinician I interviewed said she watched a coworker go from a very steady and secure job to being unemployed after a long battle with COVID-19. This coworker became a "long hauler", struggled from serious residual health concerns, exhausted her sick leave and was eventually let go because she could no longer perform required tasks.

Many essential healthcare workers struggled financially before the pandemic, then were faced with childcare and extra food costs when their children's schools closed. Others noted that their non-healthcare related partners or spouses quit their jobs in order to attend to children, which significantly diminished household income. Several clinicians I interviewed shared frustration and resentment that their salaries were cut even when they were expected to work longer and harder hours. Occasionally, a practitioner I interviewed stated that online spending became an issue, giving them both something to control and something to bring them temporary joy or relief. An administrator of a private treatment center, prior to my writing this chapter, shared the phrase "COVID Crush" with me. The term had come to describe both the deep financial impact healthcare organizations experience in general, as well as the difficulty in recruiting and maintaining staff because larger systems enticed employees away with larger salaries.

Certainly, like all other branches of the soul health tree, the true long-term impact the coronavirus pandemic will have on the financial branch of health is yet to be seen.

Your Pre- and Post-Pandemic Relationship with Money

It is our interpretation of money, our interaction with it,
where the real mischief is and where we find the real opportunity
for self-discovery and personal transformation.
—Lynne Twist

In her book, *The Soul of Money: Transforming Your Relationship with Money and Life*, author Lynne Twist emphasizes that money itself is not the problem—it isn't good or bad. But we have placed many expectations on what it can do for us and how it can make us happy. She says, that by itself, money doesn't have power. It is the meaning we place on it that causes our discomfort. Eisenstein mirrors this statement saying, "When everything is subject to money, then the scarcity of money makes everything scarce, including the basis of human life and happiness."

No doubt, many people's circumstances have changed due to the financial impact COVID-19 has had on our lives. Many more will change as the residual effects of the pandemic unfold. But like any other dark night of the soul, we can use this time to re-evaluate this branch of health and use what we learn as an opportunity to grow.

Few think of having a relationship with money. Instead, we think it is simply something we need for survival and success. It is how we interact with our financial branch of health that really defines our happiness in this part of our overall vitality. Certainly, as you look at health from a deeper perspective—the soul health perspective—you will realize that our perceptions and interactions with money can play a key role in how content we are with life.

Twist goes on to say in her book that "Rarely in our life is money a place of genuine freedom, joy, or clarity, yet we routinely allow it to dictate the terms of our lives and often to be the single most important factor in the decisions we make about work, love, family, and friendship. Below you will find a brief explanation of the five components that are explored in the Questionnaire for the Financial Branch of Health. Examining these will help you to realign your financial branch of health, which will then help you rebalance your overall tree of life.

Financial Security

The pandemic has shown that financial insecurity plays a key role in overall health. While doctors and nurses received much of the praise and sometimes increased compensation during the pandemic, they make up only twenty percent of essential healthcare workforce in our nation. The other eighty percent of front-line healthcare workers often saw the most layoffs, hours cut and the least increase in wages. According to the Society for Health Resource Management, their median pay is $13.48 an hour. That is not enough in "normal" times, let alone during a very expensive pandemic.

Our perceptions about scarcity or abundance hit the core of financial security. Our sense of security, then, depends primarily on what we perceive our needs to be and whether or not we have the means to support them.

Management of Resources

How we manage our resources, including how we save or spend, pay or don't pay bills, and how we acquire and manage debt directly reflects our relationship with money. During the pandemic, a national survey found that one in four Americans sought advice from a financial advisor for the first time ever. The conclusion was that citizens were both more concerned with their financial futures and also more interested in learning how to manage their financial branch of health.

Just like soul health in general, balancing income with financial output is the key to a more aligned life. Similar to the care of our inner self, we need more resources coming in than going out in order to enjoy a radiant life.

Spending Habits

As mentioned earlier, several of the healthcare providers I interviewed admitted they used online shopping as a means to comfort them during the pandemic. What else are you going to do for fun when the world is locked down?

When we believe we require something other than a basic need to make us happy, it may indicate that our soul is out of balance and needs some work. Unnecessary spending can lead to financial hardship and stress, which affects other branches of your tree of health. Philosopher and author, Henry David Thoreau said, "Money is not required to buy one necessity of the soul." To have a vigorous financial branch of health means that spending is in balance with the rest of your tree.

Planning for the Future

There was nothing planned about the arrival of a world health event. Certainly the last thing on many people's minds was the creation of a plan to secure their financial future. As you rebuild your tree of health, planning how your financial branch of health can look in the future will likely be a higher priority.

Our ability to both survive and thrive has everything to do with our willingness and ability to look ahead. This allows us to consider our needs, bolster our resources and plan accordingly. Saving for the future accomplishes much more than protecting us from financial crisis. It also protects our soul. By securing our financial future, we stabilize our overall tree.

Beliefs about Money

We all hold certain beliefs about money, whether healthy or not. Our beliefs are often based in how our families influenced us and our perspective on money and finances is much the same. Ideas of success, financial responsibility, appreciation for what we have, understanding of how money can help or hurt us, and financial choices in general are all woven into how we perceive and manage our financial branch of health.

While it might not seem so, financial responsibility often mirrors how we care for our soul. As we learn to take care of our inner self, we become stewards to the essence of who we are. Similarly, as we learn about our relationship with money, we become more committed to appropriately overseeing matters related to money.

Following is the Questionnaire for the Financial Branch of Health. Take a few minutes to complete the survey and explore the aspects of creating a healthier relationship with money for your soul health.

Questionnaire for the Financial Branch of Health

On a scale of 1 to 10, rate the level of your health within each area described. A 10 describes optimal, radiant health, while a 1 describes an almost complete lack of health within the given aspect of the financial branch. Remember, this questionnaire is designed to create a roadmap to overall radiant health. It is not meant to overwhelm you.

Financial Security
1._____ I feel financially secure.
2._____ I have enough money to pay my monthly bills.
3._____ I feel I will always have what I need.
4._____ I am not stressed about money.
5._____ Paying bills does not cause me stress.
6._____ I have enough resources to manage sudden expenses.

Management of Resources
1._____ I manage money well.
2._____ I do not live paycheck to paycheck.
3._____ I am free of debt.
4._____ I am comfortable with the amount of my debt.
5._____ I pay cash for most purchases.
6._____ I pay off credit cards each month.
7._____ I generally know the amount of my monthly expenses.
8._____ I can anticipate when certain extra expenses are approaching.

Spending Habits
1._____ I buy only items I can afford.
2._____ Generally, I do not spend beyond my means.
3._____ I avoid buying things impulsively.
4._____ I plan for what I purchase.
5._____ Generally, I follow a weekly or monthly budget.
6._____ I buy only what I need.
7._____ Within reason, I know when to spend money on myself as a display of self-love.

Financial Planning
1._____ I regularly save for the future.
2._____ I have planned for retirement from an early age.
3._____ I have a realistic idea of how much money I will need for retirement.
4._____ I have a plan for paying off debts.
5._____ I have a plan for spending and saving.
6._____ I understand most investment language and terms.
7._____ I have both short- and long-term financial goals.
8._____ I know how to save money through tax deductions, tax credits, and so on.

Beliefs About Money
1._____ My beliefs about money are realistic.
2._____ I know my financial resources are my responsibility.
3._____ Others would agree that I am responsible with how I spend money.
4._____ My idea of success is motivated by more than money.
5._____ I do not take money for granted.
6._____ I know that my perception of financial security affects all other aspects of my life.

Many people are surprised by their reactions to this questionnaire because they've never considered having a "relationship" with money, other than believing they need it to survive. More than ever, many healthcare workers will consider this aspect of health as essential to their overall life balance. When you carefully assess your relationship with money, you will see its impact on the relationship you have with your soul as well.

The Soulful Practice of Financial Health

Wealth is the ability to fully experience life.
–Henry David Thoreau

More and more authors are presenting the "soul" side of finance. Although there is nothing sacred about money itself, the soul of money lies in how we see it affecting our lives. Like many other stressful reactions we have had to our experience of the pandemic, our discomforting thoughts and emotions about money can eventually lead us to a more grounded and healthy way of addressing our financial condition if we take the time to explore how to do this.

In his book, *Sacred Economics*, Charles Eisenstein, describes how money has created a sense of separation from ourselves, each other and the world. He outlines how modern communities have gotten lost in concepts about money and points out how it has become a more important focus than developing a fulfilling inner life. He illustrates how the focus on finance has prevented many people from exploring inner growth and consciousness about the world outside of them.

The Three Questions of Discernment—"Is it meaningful?", "Is it necessary?" and "Does it feed my soul?"—apply to improving your financial health. While deciding what items to buy, these questions can often help you make the decision for whether the money spent yields the outcome you are looking for in making the purchase. Similarly, while planning for vacations, attending concerts and other events and accepting invitations for social engagements, these questions can assist in aligning your financial branch of health to receive the most benefit.

As healthcare workers consider their careers in medicine, discernment about money will likely become a more important factor than prior to the pandemic, whether deciding to look for a more stable job, retiring when possible or even intentionally taking a pay cut to balance other branches of their tree. In many cases, providers will realize that "less" really is more in terms of reprioritizing where you put your time and energy. The end goal will be to enhance your overall health, while more deeply assessing and fulfilling the needs of your soul.

The financial branch of health can be uncomfortable to explore for many. But once you develop a better relationship with money, you build a better relationship with yourself as well. When ready, glance through the Questionnaire for the Financial Branch of Health again and then see how the E.V.O.L.V.E. protocol can help to improve this branch of health:

E–Examine

+ How have your finances changed since the pandemic began?
+ What habits changed, helped or hindered your financial branch of health?

V–Vision

+ How do you envision your financial branch to change in the future?
+ When you envision wealth, what does that look like to you?
+ What level of financial health do you want to reach in the next 5 years?

O–Observe

+ How has your relationship with money changed?
+ What fear do you carry related to your finances?

+ What emotions arise when you think about the financial branch of health?

L–Learn

+ What did you learn about your spending habits during the pandemic?
+ What did you learn about how others handle month during this time?
+ What would you like to learn about financial management?

V–Venture

+ What new methods of managing money are you ready to try?
+ In what ways can you "stretch your financial edges" without stretching your budget?
+ What would help you build confidence in managing your financial branch of health?

E–Elevate

+ What do you need to overcome in order to reach your financial goals?
+ What would help you step into a higher earning bracket?

CHAPTER FOURTEEN

THE SEXUAL BRANCH OF HEALTH

Love During Lockdown

For the first time in history, sex is more
dangerous than the cigarette afterward.

−Jay Leno

Sexual health is usually kept quiet, including within all other wellness models I've found so far. But for many people this branch directly impacts overall radiant health, either by enhancing or diminishing it. Even among healthcare providers—the professionals expected to discuss such sensitive topics—this aspect of health is often overlooked or avoided.

Making love is the most sacred activity two individuals can share. It is also the most natural, yet vulnerable interaction we have with others. These intimate acts help us bond as well as stay connected. However, many factors must align for sex to enrich the lives of both partners and if this doesn't happen, it can actually push people apart.

COVID-19 created many obstacles to enjoying a satisfying sex life, including the simple fact that in the early months of the pandemic we didn't know if it was even safe to engage with others in this way. While comedian, Jay Leno, joked about the "dangerous" nature of sex several years prior, it is truer now than when he first shared the quote listed above.

Studies conducted during the pandemic verified that sexual activity decreased significantly, especially during the first year. This was true for both single and partnered or married individuals, with many factors playing a part in diminishing this aspect of overall health. One study indicated that having sex during the pandemic was associated with significantly lower rates of anxiety and depression, concluding that sexual intimacy had a protective affect against generalized distress. This is likely related both to the comfort one feels by being close to another and also the biological release a person experiences as they complete this sacred act.

Most of the providers I interviewed for this book skipped this question altogether. Several noted that they felt closer to their partners than prior to the arrival of the virus. A few admitted to affairs (mostly with coworkers) and quite a few noted that sexual activity was much less of a priority because responsibilities with both childcare and work had zapped what was left of the providers' energy. One provider simply answered, "Kaput", noting there had been no sexual activity at all with his spouse during the pandemic due to her concerns with contracting the virus.

Stress has long been known to lower the libido, but this all depends on the factors that impact an individual's interest, willingness and energy to engage in intimate activities.

Sex as God's Joke

Everything in the world is about sex except sex.
−Oscar Wilde

Actress Bette Davis said, "Sex is God's joke on human beings." While we can't be sure what she meant by this, we do know that sex tends to complicate relationships. Sex—or lack thereof—in a relationship tends to top the list of why couples seek therapy as well as contributing greatly to breakups and rates of divorce. The reality is, women and men often see and experience sex in vastly different ways depending on beliefs, upbringing, the meaning of sex to each, a history of sexual trauma and other factors. Therefore, each person's experience of sexual intimacy is as unique as the person's soul.

As a therapist and author of the Soul Health Model, I learned decades ago that the sexual branch of health needed to be acknowledged as a significant part of overall well-being. While the healthiest sexual branch for some may include frequent activity with a partner or spouse, no sex at all is what fulfills another's needs. In other words, some people can't go without being hot and bothered, whereas others don't want to bother with sex at all. Both are healthy expressions of sexual health, but aren't necessarily compatible if their partner's needs aren't aligned.

Author, John Gray, talks about the difference between men and women with regard to sex. He notes that men often enjoy sex as a way to release uncomfortable emotions, saying, "He is stressed by the unsolved problems of his day and finds relief through forgetting them." However, women often feel more stressed when asked to have sex, noting, "She, however, wants to find relief by talking about the problems of her day." He adds that women tend to need to release stress so they can later relax and enjoy sexual intimacy with their partners.

Biologically speaking, a difference exists as well. The "love hormone", oxytocin, is associated with sexual activity and relationship-building because levels tend to increase with hugging and orgasm. The irony for couples is that men tend to experience empathy, trust and closeness after a sexual climax with their partner, but women need to feel nurtured, loved and trusting of their partners *before* they feel ready to engage in this way. While men might experience sexual activity as a stress reliever, a woman often finds it as an inducer of elevated stress if her emotional needs aren't supported first. This obviously serves as an obstacle when the needs of a partner seem to be in direct opposition to our own, thus, potentially creating issues among other branches of our tree of life.

The stress of the pandemic, no doubt, wreaked havoc on the sex lives of everyone, including healthcare practitioners. While we will likely never know the extent of "damage" the pandemic inflicted on the sexual branch of health, it is likely that this aspect of our well-being significantly altered many people's overall health.

In his books, Gray emphasizes that sexuality is only one part of intimacy with another, but one that assists in bonding with a mate for life. He says, "The soul is who you are when you strip away the body, mind, and heart. Your soul has a potential that takes an entire lifetime to be fully realized. When a couple are soul mates, when their souls recognize and love each other and they are attracted to each other physically, emotionally, and mentally, then this love not only can last but can continue to grow and become richer as the years pass. This does not mean that everything will flow easily and effortlessly. It simply means the relationship has the potential to be successful."

Following is the Questionnaire for the Sexual Branch of Health. Consider the questions to assess what changed for you during the pandemic and how you would like to rebalance this branch of health in the future. In my experience as a therapist, many people think they know more about sex than they actually do. While working for a student health promotion department during graduate school, I became quite comfortable speaking to groups about safe sex and healthy practices. This benefitted me as a therapist since clients often don't feel they can speak to anyone else about their concerns. Even as healthcare providers, many of you may feel uncomfortable talking about sexual intimacy with others. Perhaps more than ever, this is the time to explore what you do and don't know, both about the physical and emotional aspects of sexual health.

Questionnaire for the Sexual Branch of Health

On a scale of 1 to 10, rate the level of your health within each area described. A 10 describes optimal, radiant health, while a 1 describes an almost complete lack of health within the given aspect of the sexual branch. Remember, this questionnaire is designed to create a roadmap to overall radiant health. It is not meant to overwhelm you.

Knowledge
1. _____ I know what it means to engage in sex.
2. _____ I am knowledgeable about sexual practices.
3. _____ I am knowledgeable about sexual anatomy and sexual responses.
4. _____ I know my body and its sexual responses.
5. _____ I understand how I developed my beliefs and attitudes about sex.
6. _____ I know what I like and don't like when it comes to sex.
7. _____ I know how to prevent an unwanted pregnancy.
8. _____ I know what a sexually-transmitted disease is and how to prevent it.

Safety
1. _____ I know what safe sex is.
2. _____ I engage only in safe sex.
3. _____ I never wonder if I have been unsafe with a sexual partner.
4. _____ I have received adequate education about safe sex.
5. _____ I take precautions to prevent unwanted pregnancies.
6. _____ I take precautions to prevent sexually transmitted diseases.
7. _____ I always talk to sex partners about their sexual health before engaging in sex with them.

Security
1. _____ I feel emotionally secure when engaging in sex.
2. _____ I feel physically secure when engaging in sex.
3. _____ I have sex only with partners I trust.
4. _____ I can communicate freely with my partner(s) about sex.
5. _____ I know and respect my own sexual boundaries.
6. _____ I know and respect the sexual boundaries of others.
7. _____ I feel good about my sexuality.
8. _____ I feel good about expressing myself sexually with my partner(s).

Beliefs about Sex
1. _____ I have healthy beliefs about sex.
2. _____ I do not feel guilty about sex.
3. _____ I do not feel ashamed of sex.
4. _____ My beliefs about sex do not interfere with how I feel about other aspects of my life.
5. _____ I enjoy sex.
6. _____ I feel good about my sex life.
7. _____ I am aware that self-love is the key to all healthy sexual activity.

Past Experiences
1. _____ I have consented to all of my sexual experiences.
2. _____ I have only positive memories of my sexual experiences.
3. _____ My past sexual experiences have not negatively affected my sex life.
4. _____ I have sought help to resolve issues related to past negative sexual experiences.
5. _____ I feel at peace with all past sexual experiences.

Exploring the items on this questionnaire will likely give you a better idea about your sexual health and your comfort in talking with others about their own. To help you explore each category further, I've elaborated on each topic below.

Knowledge

I tell clients that "What you don't know won't hurt you" doesn't apply to sex. Few people receive adequate sex education and even fewer speak with professionals who could help them understand their sexual health, which is unique to them. What we learn about sex usually comes from peers, television, movies, books and even social media. Although a general understanding of sex is necessary for a satisfying relationship to occur, it takes much more than this to create a bond that supports soul health. To enjoy a fully soulful sexual relationship with someone, you must understand not only the general mechanics of sex, you must also understand that emotional/psychological, interpersonal and spiritual factors affect this branch of health as well. In other words, soulful sex requires a healthy balance of likenesses between the many branches of our tree of life with those of our partner.

Safety

While some studies reported lower rates of sexual activity during the pandemic, unwanted sexual contact increased in some cases for both children and adults. Safety in a soulful sexual relationship cannot be stressed enough and it has as much to do with emotional security as with possible physical risks. Several factors play a part in the safety of sexual partnerships, including good communication, healthy boundaries, personal integrity, equality, respect and unconditionality. If any of these are missing from your sexual relationship, this branch of health will inevitably be negatively impacted.

Security

Emotional security is essential in enjoying healthy, soulful sex. However, all too often, people engage in sex even if they don't feel emotionally safe or spiritually connected with their spouse or partner. Feeling pressured to engage in sex, holding onto unhealed sexual trauma and the lack of open and honest communication with your partner about needs, likes, dislikes and interest in sex all contribute to sexual insecurity. Learning to honor your deepest ally—your soul—to address these concerns will no doubt lead to healthier and more soulful sex life with your partner.

Beliefs about Sex

What we were taught or what was modeled to us during childhood influences what we believe about sexual relations in the present. Our sexual beliefs are also shaped by our culture or religion as well as societal values, gender roles and the media. Sexual trauma and our ability to heal from it also play a role in what we believe about sexual intimacy. Exploring your beliefs about sexual activity can help to create a soulful relationship with yourself so you can also enjoy one with your partner.

Past Experiences

These days, it is hard to find someone who hasn't had a sexual experience that negatively affected their overall sexual health. Unfortunately, these experiences have diminished both our willingness to discuss sexual health and our ability to enjoy a soulful sexual connection. Whatever the past created for us, it is inevitable that it affects our present and future. The path to healing beyond the pandemic may also give you the opportunity to heal beyond past sexual wounds and misalignments.

Soulful Sex Beyond the Pandemic

The body can become a vehicle to that which is beyond body,
and sex energy can become a spiritual force.
−Osho

Sex has always been a powerful force in human life and the meaning behind it has changed significantly as we've grown. It greatly affects and alters our experience of the human condition, regardless if sex is positive or negative in an individual's life. Whether you have too much, too little, or just enough, the sexual branch of health affects all others. While this is true, it is also true that this is the least discussed aspect of overall health.

Many aspects of the human condition can directly impact sexual health—many of which were more present than ever during the pandemic. Stress, grief, trauma, depression, anxiety, changes in health status, job changes, relocations, general safety, lack of energy and relationships issues are just some of the factors that likely impacted this branch of health. The experience of healthy sex is complex enough, let alone with additional layers of concern the pandemic has brought.

Like learning about the other branches, it is essential to practice discernment when rebalancing or rebuilding your sexual branch of health. Ask yourself:

- *Is sexual activity with your partner **meaningful**?* When you engage in sexual activity, is it soulful and satisfying? Do you feel deeply connected and safe with your partner?
- *Is sexual activity **necessary**?* While sexual intimacy can be an important part of a soulful relationship, it is important to recognize whether it is helping or hurting your connection to engage in sex. If you feel pressured to engage in sex, it might be more necessary to maintain a boundary that better suites your own soul. The word "necessary" is tricky when applying discernment to all branches of health, but when it comes to sexual health it is important to honor your inner self to maintain overall soul health.
- *Does sexual activity **feed your soul**?* It is true that sex can reduce stress for some, but unless it also feeds your soul, sexual activity might diminish your overall health more than enhance it. Having sex for the sake of enjoyment is one thing, but having soulful sex improves many other branches of health.

Like all other branches of health, your exploration of how to improve your sexual branch of health on your healing path can help to deepen your understanding of overall health. When the time feels right, take another look at the Questionnaire for the Sexual Branch of Health in this chapter. See how you can use the E.V.O.L.V.E. protocol to improve this branch of health:

E–Examine

+ How comfortable are you in exploring this branch of health?
+ Does anything in your past hinder your sexual branch of health?
+ Is this branch of health important to your overall health?

V–Vision

+ What is your vision of a healthy and satisfying sex life?
+ When you envision a better sex life, what is different than what you have now?

O–Observe

+ What insecurities do you have related to your sexual branch of health?
+ What would you like to understand more about this branch of health?
+ What emotions arise when you think about sexuality?

L–Learn

+ What do you need to learn about the sexual branch of health to improve it?
+ What do you need to learn about yourself and what brings you pleasure?
+ What do you need to unlearn or outgrow in order to improve this branch of health?

V—Venture

+ What are you willing to do to improve your sexual branch of health?
+ Is there something different you'd like to try in order to have a more fulfilling sex life?
+ What would help you build confidence in this area of health?

E—Elevate

+ What do you need to heal or *evolve beyond* in order to enjoy sexual health?
+ How could you change how you think to improve your sexual branch of health?

As mentioned, no other wellness model fully acknowledges the importance of sexual health. While each person differs in what they need in a healthy sexual branch of health, it is important to explore what you do and don't need to balance this aspect of your life.

CHAPTER FIFTEEN

THE SPIRITUAL BRANCH OF HEALTH
The Soul of Healing

The soul always knows what to do to heal itself.
—Carolyn Myss

The Soul Health Model already emphasizes the soulful nature of healing. However, a discussion about spirituality is still warranted as you create and embark on your healing path to post-COVID recovery.

To know your soul—the essence of who you are—and to know its deepest needs is the only true way to align your life for radiant living. Therefore, knowing your inner self *is* the only way to know true health— and the only way to pave the way to finding, reclaiming and restoring your inner light.

Throughout this book, you've been encouraged to take an inner inventory of what does and doesn't work in your life by listening to your gut reactions, your inner voice and your deepest stirrings. The light within you constantly communicates, letting you know you are on the right path. When COVID hit, your attention went into survival mode—addressing whatever you needed to do at work and home to stay afloat. Now, it is time to once again tune into that inner ally to guide and center you for your healing on the path ahead.

As you begin to settle back into your life post-pandemic, you will need something to anchor you. French philosopher, Simone Weil said, "To be rooted is perhaps the most important and least recognized need of the human soul." In the case of recovering from your experiences with the coronavirus pandemic, your soul will serve as that root or anchor. It will not lead you astray.

Soul-based living requires an awareness and conscious appreciation of how our inner wisdom can guide our lives. By paying attention to our voice from within, we can live much more simply as well as more easily. We just have to listen and heed the message. As mentioned in a previous chapter, our heads can lead us down a wrong path by overthinking situations, our hearts can tug toward decisions that aren't for our highest or overall good, but our soul never leads us down an unhealthy or incorrect road. We've all experienced the times when we've ignored what our gut reactions tell us, only to find ourselves in a bigger dilemma than before. However, when we learn to tune in and listen to our inner self, we navigate down our path without disruption.

Modern definitions of spirituality come from the words "inspire" or "in spirit". So it makes sense that our innermost ally—the voice of our soul—can serve as our ideal inspiration for how to align our lives to enjoy overall health. When we are not aligned or inspired by life, how do we feel? Distressed? Uncomfortable? *Dis*-eased?

Letting our souls lead our lives brings an unmistakable awareness of how life works best for us, offering meaning and fulfillment through everything we experience. We cannot be spiritually healthy without being conscious of our place and impact in the world. Although the Soul Health Model already holds spiritual implications, it is the intentional commitment to a spiritually healthy life that allows the rest of the branches to thrive. This intention also allows us to grow both through the challenges of the human condition and as the essence of who we are—our soul.

Spiritual Health and Your Healing Path

We are in this life to enlarge the soul,
liberate the spirit and light up the brain.
—Tom Robbins

Spirituality is making a comeback in modern healthcare with hundreds of articles and books noting the importance of spiritual health in the lives and recoveries of medical patients. Eighty-one percent of individuals report that their primary coping mechanism includes spiritual practices when they are sick. Also, up to ninety-four percent of patients wish their healthcare providers would address spirituality as part of their regular doctor visits. Unfortunately, less than ten percent actually do so. Regardless of this lack of formal attention in medical care, research clearly shows that spirituality has a generally positive and protective effect on overall health—coping, social support, healthy behaviors, reduction of anxiety and depression, positive outlook on healing, increased survival rates, acceleration of recovery, reduction of regret and general satisfaction and appreciation for life. Research clearly indicates that those who do not have a spiritual life tend to have more negative health outcomes.

Religion and spirituality are not synonymous and differ in both what they mean and how you practice. You can have one without the other, both or neither in your life. When I explain the difference to others, I keep it simple: religion is created for us and we create our own spirituality. We can follow a belief system or religion that is already established. However, our spirituality is completely our own—something manifestly more personal, necessary and meaningful and that which feeds our soul more than any formalized process we might follow. Religion tends to be somewhat exclusive—separating us from other formal belief systems, while spirituality is inclusive in nature—acknowledging that although each person is on their own path, we are all on a similar journey of self-discovery. Religion is seen as a way of *doing*—following a specific dogma or set of rituals, while spirituality is most often described as a way of *being*—embracing life and its meaning through everything we experience including each breath, thought and action. Thus, we aren't necessarily religious if we are spiritual and vice versa. You can be both or one without the other.

It is clear that those who hold strong spiritual beliefs rely on them while coping with stress and illness. However, in my experience as a therapist, I'm also aware that we can experience a spiritual crisis when life goes down an unexpected and painful path. Much like the dark night of the soul mentioned earlier in this book, many people's belief systems are shaken when faced with crisis—in this case a global health event. I've helped numerous clients heal from what can be called "God trauma" or "church hurt"—an existential shift away from one's previously held beliefs due to what is perceived as betrayal or shock that our higher power could create such unfathomable and painful circumstances. I can assume that many people—including you as healthcare providers—might experience this as you try to make sense of your experiences throughout the pandemic.

Just like your soul, your spirituality is yours and yours alone. The uniqueness of your spiritual branch of health will mirror the uniqueness of your soul. No other's spiritual beliefs and practices will ever be like your own. A willingness to pay attention to your inner self and understand its message is an essential part of building the foundation for your healing path. As you exercise your ability to rebuild your life, your understanding of overall soul health will deepen and you will experience enhanced vitality as you develop beyond your pre-COVID self.

Following is the Questionnaire for the Spiritual Branch of Health. As you explore your responses, take some time to envision and elevate your experience of spiritual wellbeing. Think about how this will influence and enhance the other branches of health. You might also want to pay attention to how your current spiritual health is different from what it was pre-COVID. This will help you identify areas that might need to be addressed—cleaned out or filled up—on your healing path.

Questionnaire for the Spiritual Branch of Health

On a scale of 1 to 10, rate the level of your health within each area described. A 10 describes optimal, radiant health, while a 1 describes an almost complete lack of health within the given aspect of the spiritual branch. Remember, this questionnaire is designed to create a roadmap to overall radiant health. It is not meant to overwhelm you.

Sense of Inner Peace
1._____ Spirituality is important to me.
2._____ I have good spiritual wellness.
3._____ I have inner peace.
4._____ I actively seek ways to create inner peace.
5._____ I can find inner peace without using unhealthy substances.
6._____ I know when I need to re-center or ground myself.
7._____ Feeling inner peace allows me to live my life more effectively.
8._____ I know what it takes to help me find inner peace.

Beliefs about Spirituality and Religion
1._____ I know the difference between spirituality and religion.
2._____ I feel good about my spiritual and/or religious beliefs.
3._____ I feel safe sharing my beliefs with others.
4._____ I find peace in my spiritual beliefs.
5._____ I am clear about my spiritual beliefs.
6._____ My spiritual beliefs are healthy for me and others around me.
7._____ I find meaning and purpose through my spiritual beliefs.
8._____ My spiritual beliefs do not leave me feeling conflicted or guilty.

Spiritual Practices
1._____ I actively practice my spiritual beliefs.
2._____ I practice my beliefs on a daily basis.
3._____ The people in my life support my spiritual practices.
4._____ My spiritual practices enhance inner peace and strength.
5._____ I know when I need to spend more time in my spiritual practices to feel more balanced or well.
6._____ I actively seek to learn more about my spirituality.
7._____ My spiritual activities are an important part of my daily life.

World View
1._____ I accept others' spiritual beliefs.
2._____ I recognize that it is okay to have different spiritual beliefs from others.
3._____ I am open to learning about other people's spiritual beliefs and practices.
4._____ I do not impose my spiritual beliefs on others.
5._____ I believe I am part of a larger whole or picture.
6._____ I know I can learn from others' spiritual beliefs and practices, even if they aren't my own.

Soul Awareness
1._____ I know clarity increases when I listen to my soul.
2._____ I accept troublesome events as opportunities for soul growth.
3._____ I am aware of what my soul needs in order to feel spiritually well.
4._____ When I listen, I can hear my inner voice in every moment.
5._____ I know when my soul feels stagnant and when it is evolving.

How has an awareness of your soul—your inner self—changed since before the arrival of the coronavirus? What is different since starting to read this book?

This branch of health is as multidimensional as the other branches within the Soul Health Model—possibly even more so. Regardless of your spiritual or religious beliefs, a conscious awareness of soul health helps you to see the interconnectedness of all aspects of who you are and allows you to reach a deeper and richer level of overall health.

Inner Peace

Who doesn't want to feel more contentment and peace in their lives? Inner peace is described as a state of being mentally and spiritually calm and centered, even in the face of discord or stress. Although this might seem impossible—particularly during or after a pandemic—fostering a strong branch of spiritual health allows us to experience inner balance regardless of our circumstances. What brings an individual peace is also an individual process—one that is as unique as that person's soul.

Beliefs About Spirituality and Religion

Religion is based on a set of concepts held in common and practiced by a group of people, whereas spirituality is grounded in an individual's understanding of what brings them contentment and peace. A person's spiritual branch of health can include a mixture of spiritual and religious beliefs and traditions. The health of this branch depends on how comfortable the person feels with those principles. While religious beliefs generally stay the same, spiritual ones can change to include new and expanded ideas or eliminate those that no longer fit.

Spiritual Practices

While religious practices are conducted as part of a community, there is nothing more personal than the spiritual practices we adopt. When we routinely practice our individual spirituality, we tend to feel more engaged with life, find more meaning, live with greater appreciation and remain aware of how we affect the world and how it affects us. Because spiritual practices vary widely—prayer, meditation, yoga, recitation of mantras, singing, dancing, communing with nature, discussion groups, etc.—our active participation strengthens and enhances our spiritual branch of health.

Worldview

It seems like COVID-19 tested us in developing a more spiritual worldview. Having a healthy spiritual view of the world means that you accept and value both your beliefs and those of others. This is not easy when our views differ widely, especially as we've found during the pandemic. Highly spiritual people have no need to judge others. Instead, they welcome differing ideas and cherish the opportunity to learn about others regardless of whether they agree. People with a healthy and enlightened spiritual branch of health have no need to impose their spiritual ideas on others and remain open to learning about belief systems outside of their own. No doubt, the worldview of many will, or has changed since the beginning of the pandemic and will warrant some exploration as they embark on their healing path.

Soul Awareness

Most of us aren't taught to listen to our soul, yet, how different would our existence be if we did? How much easier would life be if we heeded the instructions of our internal navigation system? An awareness of our inner self, appreciation for the wisdom it has to offer and a commitment to fulfilling our deep spiritual needs always leads to both radiant health and profound inner peace. Consciousness about our inner ally allows us to find more meaning and purpose in each of our actions and decisions. It also creates a moment-to-moment awareness of what we need in order to best align our lives.

Spirituality is what you create for yourself whereas religion is created for you. Take some time to explore the Questionnaire for the Spiritual Branch of Health using the E.V.O.L.V.E. protocol to help you further develop your personalized approach to spirituality:

E–Examine

+ How have my beliefs and practices changed since the pandemic began?
+ Do I have "church hurt" or "God trauma" that needs to be healed?
+ How have my spiritual beliefs changed since I was young?

V–Vision

+ How do you envision your relationship with God, Spirit, the Universe—whatever word fits your spiritual language?
+ As you think about the future, how do you envision your spirituality changing?

O–Observe

+ Do you have discomfort in exploring your spiritual branch of health?
+ How do I feel about my current beliefs?
+ Is there something you feel you'd like to incorporate into your life to enhance your spiritual health?

L–Learn

+ What would you like to learn about in order to explore spiritual health?
+ What spiritual practices would you like to learn more about?
+ What have you already learned about yourself related to your spiritual branch of health?

V–Venture

+ Are there any books you've been wanting to read in order to improve your spiritual health?
+ Is there a new church or spiritual center you'd like to visit?

+ How would you practice your spirituality differently if you could?

E–Elevate

+ What would help you grow in terms of your spiritual development?
+ How could you "up your game" in terms of how you practice your spirituality?

CHAPTER SIXTEEN

RECREATIONAL HEALTH
The Re-Creation of Recreation

When you do things from your soul,
you feel a river moving in you, a joy.
–RUMI

Fun is food for the soul. It nourishes us so we can soften the challenges of the human condition. Without fun, our inner light will diminish and even die, causing depression, anxiety, worry and other forms of *dis*-ease. In the case of the pandemic, many, especially healthcare workers experienced extreme distress, exhaustion and heartache, leaving very little room or time for fun and leisure.

Years before I created the Soul Health Model, I said my first book would be about how to help adults play again. Early in my adulthood, I observed how few people seem to prioritize fun as part of their overall self-care. It appears that the more "advanced" society becomes, the more we rush to keep up and the less time we make to restore our inner selves. We also tend to look for joy outside of ourselves, opting to choose actual food and drink as replacements for feeding our souls with fun.

Instead of writing a book about how to have more fun, I wrote about the soul, which in fact, is about acknowledging and claiming the soul's most natural state—contentment and joy. While there has been nothing fun or leisurely about the pandemic, it is likely that seeking joy was a primary factor in helping you survive. It will undoubtedly also be an essential component in restoring you while on your healing path.

As I interviewed healthcare workers for this book, I got more than a subtle glimpse into their lives. Along with the stories of heartache they shared, some practitioners offered explanations of how they created joy in their not so joyful worlds. Like the general public, many practitioners spoke of online happy hours, playing with household pets, long hours of binge-watching Netflix movies or live stream events and the resurrection of old board games and jigsaw puzzles. But some became a bit more creative in how they inserted fun and leisure into their less than joyful circumstances.

One physician family created outdoor movie nights for friends and neighbors, projecting films on the side of their house. They served popcorn, candy, soda, nachos and other movie favorites to complete the scene—all groups of attendees spaced at least six feet apart.

A yoga instructor decided to spread joy in her neighborhood by planting an expansive flower garden in front of her house. She posted a sign with some kid-safe scissors attached to invite those who passed by to take a flower a day to share with their friends and loved ones at home. The instructor smiled as she watched both children and adults enjoy their daily stop for a flower and received even more joy as she wondered who would receive the blossom the visitors cut. She received thank you notes and cards throughout the months to follow.

I heard about "food swaps"—practitioners who like to cook would set up exchange events with friends and family so they could continue to enjoy each other's food even if they couldn't enjoy their company.

Several providers took up gardening, arts and crafts, painting and other hobbies. One joked that she often flashed to her past as she started making macramé projects again—something that has actually become quite vogue again.

Whatever the steps providers took, it was clear they were forced to become more creative with how they integrated recreation into their pandemic lives.

The Joy-Filled Soul

If you are losing your leisure, look out; you may be losing your soul.
—Logan Smith

As a psychologist, I spend my days trying to help people find their joy again—and sometimes for what they perceive as the very first time. The human condition dishes out a lot of stress, turmoil, disappointment, grief and more as we navigate this thing we call life. Add a global health event to the mix and you can bet that whatever joy and contentment was there to begin with most likely diminished or evaporated all together.

Our soul is *nothing* without joy. We need it to remind us of why we are alive. It is the light that draws us forward and keeps us aware that something is on the other side of the darkness. In the times when the human condition has darkened our view, the experience of joy can seem impossible to access, which means that our ability to hear our soul is diminished as well. These dark nights, when we can't see or feel our inner light—the joy within—are the times when we most lose touch with the essence of who we are. Our lives get off track, we lose our way and we often feel we can no longer recognize who we are. We become disconnected from our soul.

Therefore, our sense of joy—or lack of it—serves as another measure of our overall soul health. Our ability to feel joy and contentment is much like the pilot light for our inner self; if it stays lit we can experience at least some pleasure in life, which allows us to tolerate the darker sides of the human condition. However, if our light is dimmed or snuffed out, nothing seems to matter—including oneself.

Awareness of how fun feeds our soul and brings us joy is essential in attaining optimal health. Although what we do for fun doesn't fully define us, the interplay between our ten branches of health—including how well we attend to fun and leisure—do reflect the health of our soul. We will never find our way on our healing path if we don't understand how recreational health plays an integral part in finding our light beyond the darkness.

There is more to fun and leisure than simply doing something that makes us laugh or relax. The meaning we place on our activities often deepens the restorative aspects of our recreational health. With this in mind, it is particularly helpful to apply the *Three Questions of Discernment* as you learn to improve your recreational branch of health. Deciding whether an activity is meaningful, necessary and/or feeds your soul can make all the difference in enhancing this vital part of your life.

The Art and Science of Soul-Care

Rebuild your strength, Regain your balance, Revive your energy, Refresh your mind, Rekindle your soul.
—Buddha Groove

No formal research is necessary to prove that healthcare practitioners' overall health declined during the pandemic. Even less is needed to demonstrate that fun and leisure suffered. The recreational branch of soul health relates to both the fun *and* the leisure we allow, invite or create in our lives and a lack of either directly diminishes our inner light. Integrating fun activities into our life helps to offset the challenges of the human condition, while leisure activities provide respite from our personal and professional responsibilities. Including both fun and leisure as part of our overall health is necessary in fortifying our inner self and promoting our evolution beyond the most challenging parts of the human condition.

However, most people don't make or take time for fun. A 2016 survey showed that over half (54%) of Americans who work in the United States choose not to use all of their allowable vacation time. The standard for long work hours was no doubt exacerbated by employer expectations during the pandemic.

A more recent study showed that in 2020, one in four (26%) U.S. respondents noted that they hadn't taken a vacation in over a year, compared to 16% in 2019. The same study also showed that forty-two percent of individuals cancelled one or more trips due to COVID-19.

Research also shows that the risk of serious health conditions and shortened life spans increases for those who don't take time off for vacations. In fact, a study indicated that men who had taken no vacation within the preceding five years had the highest incidence of heart disease of those surveyed. The good news is that the men who took annual vacations reduced their risk of death by 20%.

Neurological studies have also been conducted to determine how our brains form neural pathways according to whether or not we slow down to take time for ourselves. One researcher found that those who don't take time from their daily routines to relax actually find it harder to do so on the rare day off since the neural pathway that produces feelings of calm and peacefulness becomes weaker. This makes it increasingly more difficult to adjust to a less stressful state of being when given the chance. This provides proof that our body needs regular fun and leisure to protect and sustain our overall and optimal health.

There is clear and consistent evidence that fun and leisure shows positive enhancement of health. These activities decrease depression, anxiety and fatigue as well as reduce the likelihood of burnout and low job satisfaction. Recreation also promotes creativity, improves mental function, strengthens social support and increases performance and productivity.

Below is the Questionnaire for the Recreational Branch of Health. When the time feels right, evaluate your own ideas of fun and leisure as well as how they have affected your soul health. As you answer, consider how your recreational branch of health appeared prior to the pandemic as well. Sometimes this reminds you of activities you once enjoyed that you can integrate into your life again. You might have added some creative ways to enjoy fun and leisure during the pandemic; now you can see how this has enhanced your recreational branch of health.

Questionnaire for the Recreational Branch of Health

On a scale of 1 to 10, rate the level of your health within each area described. A 10 describes optimal, radiant health, while a 1 describes an almost complete lack of health within the given aspect of the recreational branch. Remember, this questionnaire is designed to create a roadmap to overall radiant health. It is not meant to overwhelm you.

Fun
1._____ I have enough fun in my life.
2._____ I know what is fun to me.
3._____ I take time to have fun.
4._____ I laugh often.
5._____ I play often.
6._____ I am playful with others.
7._____ Others think I am fun.

Leisure
1._____ I know how to relax.
2._____ I have enough leisure time.
3._____ I actively seek time to relax.
4._____ I plan ahead for time away from work.
5._____ I use all vacation time that is allotted to me.
6._____ I use my weekends to relax.
7._____ I engage in healthy activities that put me at ease.
8._____ Leisure time is a high priority for me.

Balance
1._____ I maintain a good balance between work and leisure.
2._____ I actively work to create and maintain balance in my life.
3._____ I rarely feel physically or emotionally drained.
4._____ Most people would say I have a well-balanced life.
5._____ I know when to take a break from busy or stressful activities.
6._____ I plan ahead for busy or stressful times when I know I will need leisure time.

Beliefs about Fun and Leisure
1._____ Fun and leisure are important to me.
2._____ I know it is okay to have fun.
3._____ I know it is okay for others to have fun.
4._____ I know it is okay to need and take time to rest.
5._____ I am comfortable with having fun.
6._____ I am comfortable with having down time or leisure.
7._____ I know that fun and leisure are important for overall health.
8._____ I know that allowing fun and leisure into my life is a sure sign of self-love.

Outlook on Life
1._____ I can laugh at myself.
2._____ I try not to take life too seriously.
3._____ I look for ways to see the bright side in life.
4._____ I stop to notice the things happening around me that are fun and entertaining.
5._____ I can find joy in even the little things.

The Questionnaire for the Recreational Branch of Health might have included aspects of fun and leisure that you never considered before. As you learn more about how to improve this branch, you will come to understand how to better feed your soul. Your willingness to explore how recreation assists in overall well-being will also enhance your ability to handle the inevitable stressors of the human condition.

Fun

Do you know how to "behave playfully"? Fun—or our ability to play—is highly underrated among adults. As our responsibilities increase, our pursuit of fun tends to decrease. This leaves our energy tanks empty and our lights dimmed. Fun enhances health by moderating many common health concerns (blood pressure, heart disease, muscle tension, headaches, etc.) while boosting immunity, protecting against mental health conditions and promoting better overall physical health.

Leisure

Most people long for time to slow down, but rarely create the opportunity to do so. Unfortunately, as a result, relaxation has become a lost art. Despite the fact that time away—vacations or other deliberate periods of leisure—improve clarity, problem solving and hopefulness about stressful situations, few people take the time they need to hear the voice of their soul. Instead, even on their time off, many people neglect the need for leisure in their lives. However, with just a little time spent in "airing out" your soul, you can rekindle a connection with your inner ally.

Balance

The whole concept of soul health suggests that life balance is the key to optimal living. Few people factor fun and leisure into their quest for health. The truth is, your balance will not find you; you must create it. In fact, both fun and leisure can be used to enhance all branches of health—not just the recreational branch. This is the art and science of soul-care—artfully creating joy and contentment in all aspects of well-being.

Beliefs about Fun and Leisure

In our society, it is common to feel guilty about including fun and leisure into daily life. While many cultures embrace time for fun and time to relax, the United States seems to have forgotten the importance of living a more leisurely lifestyle. Values about recreation are instilled both by those who influenced us when young and by the environment in which we were raised. A strong work ethic will not, alone, feed your soul. Because recreational health plays an essential part in overall health, it is important to look at it as a necessary and meaningful part of life.

Outlook on Life

Whether thinking about overall soul health or simply the recreational branch, the way you look at life is how you will experience it. If your outlook includes a bright light at the end, you will gravitate toward activities that will help you get there. While the human condition forces us to take life seriously, you have to remember that our soul's most natural state is joy and contentment. As we find the lighter side of our trials and tribulations, we can reach a more balanced and radiant destination on our journey.

When we understand the need to enhance and maintain our recreational branch of health, we begin to master the art and soul of self-care. We realize that even our activities related to fun and leisure take a necessary role in overall health, adding deeper meaning to how we tend to this branch. When we invest in healthy recreation, we feed our souls in such a way that healing is ensured on our path to recovery.

Recreational health inevitably took a major hit during the pandemic. Take a look again at the Questionnaire for the Recreational Branch of Health. When ready, explore how the E.V.O.L.V.E. protocol can be used to enhance or reclaim this important branch of health:

E–Examine

+ What aspects of recreational health did you miss the most during the pandemic?
+ What would you most like to reintegrate into your life to improve your fun and leisure?
+ How did my needs change related to recreational health?

V–Vision

+ How do you envision your optimal recreational health to look like in the future?
+ What parts of recreational health will grow the most as I improve my overall tree of life?
+ How can I envision fun and leisure being an everyday part of my life?

O–Observe

+ What do you believe about having fun and enjoying leisure?
+ What are my priorities in terms of work-life balance?
+ What will I regret *not* doing more of in the future?

L–Learn

+ What did you learn about your recreational branch of health during the pandemic?
+ Is there any fun or leisure activity that you want to try and/or learn about?

V–Venture

+ How can you increase the amount of time you spend on your recreational branch of health?
+ Is there a new hobby or fun activity you've been wanting to try?
+ Are there fun classes you'd like to take?

E–Elevate

+ How would you "elevate" your recreational branch of health if you could?

+ What activities of fun and leisure would help you "up your game" as part of your recreational health?

+ Fun and leisure might be an underrated part of life, but joy is the soul's most natural state. This means that the more you prioritize recreational health, the more you will experience overall radiant living.

PART THREE
THE HEALING PATH

You have to grow from the inside out.
None can teach you, none can make you spiritual.
There is no other teacher but your own soul.

—Swami Vivekananda

CHAPTER SEVENTEEN
THE GOLDEN PATH

Walk on your own yellow brick road. If you can't
find one, spray paint your way into happiness.
If that doesn't work, buy yellow shoes.

—SADIQUA HAMDAN

Inspirational writer, Sadiqua Hamdan urges us to get creative in finding our healing path through her words in the above quote. What other option do we have after our world was shaken under such unexpected and unfathomable circumstances?

By this point in the book, you likely already have a general idea about which of the branches on your tree of life need attention as well as how they are all interrelated. Now it is time to begin creating your personalized path to healing. Although I mentioned before that healthcare providers have a protocol or procedure for everyone but themselves, a one-size fits all approach will not fix what was wounded or broken during your experience of the coronavirus pandemic. Your healing path is up to you to design. With the help of the Soul Health Model and the other ideas and tools provided in this book, you will have what you need to creatively pave your way back to light.

The yellow brick road in the Wizard of Oz has come to represent far more than a path with bricks. It is seen as the path that leads to something better, with many lessons to be learned along the way. To modern Buddhists, this road is described as the path to enlightenment. On her journey, Dorothy met many others who were also looking for something they felt was missing or broken and together they made it to the end. There was a happy ending for all of them. But now, it is you who needs to rebuild and restore your vitality to reach a more radiant life than what you've experienced since the beginning of your darkened days. Other than the scary flying monkeys, the memory of the story of Oz almost always brings both triumph and comfort.

Your own light at the end—and path to enlightenment—is your healing path. It is your soul's journey out of the darkness and into a much brighter light and future. Just as a storm created the circumstances for Dorothy's unexpected adventures and chance meetings with those who became long-term friends, the coronavirus storm took us all by surprise. Many of you already appreciate some of the situations and people who unexpectedly enhanced—and possibly sustained your light during the pandemic. The three helpers that Dorothy found along the way represent three primary virtues that you will need on your own healing journey.

Curiosity for Life

The Scarecrow wants nothing more than to have a brain. You already have them—very good ones—but they have been far overworked, stressed and fogged by what you've been through. In the story of Oz, the Scarecrow's quest represents the need for an inquisitive nature and healthy curiosity for life. Our personal growth and evolution rarely go as planned and it is often the most challenging events in our lives that bring the most meaning once we have the time and space to examine and reflect upon our experiences. Allowing yourself to explore how you've changed as a result of the pandemic will allow you to go to the source of where the real change begins—through your inner self—your soul. The deepest part of you wants you to rise above the darkness to adopt that curiosity about how you will get to a new and brighter ending. That light within is the motivating factor that will help you to wonder, "What if I could feel better?" "How can I heal from my experiences to reach a new level of understanding, appreciation and luminosity in life?" "What if there really is light at the end?"

Over the last several decades, the study of consciousness—the state of being awake and aware of one's surroundings and internal world—has brought most scientists to understand that this presence in the moment has more to do with the soul than it does the brain. Physician and author, Larry Dossey says, "The cognitive structure does not generate consciousness; it simply reflects it; and in the process limits and embellishes it." He, like many others, has concluded that something deeper within us is at the core of both our existence and our drive to survive. He notes that learning to live beyond the brain is the real key to our evolution saying, "Transcendence is the only real alternative to extinction."

Thus, your path to healing will require you to go deeper to explore how your experiences can help you rise above once typical ways of coping, while utilizing a healthy curiosity about how you can grow beyond your previously known self. Discomfort always accompanies evolution. Let your curious nature help you take the first steps down your path to healing.

Compassion

In the Wizard of Oz, the Tin Man lacked a heart. He yearned to gain a caring and loving nature. He thought this would help him relate to others, but what he found during the story is that it also helped him be more compassionate and caring toward himself.

Healthcare workers have a knack for taking care of others, but are rather deficient in caring for themselves. While dedication to others is a noble quality, it can also leave the giver feeling quite hollow and drained. In order to heal your deepest inner self, you must practice self- love and self-compassion. But this is often the biggest challenge for those trained to help others.

Psychologist and mindful self-compassion expert, Christopher Germer says, "Self-compassion is simply giving the same kindness to ourselves that we would give to others." It is interesting that most healthcare workers are adept at taking care of those around them, but often feel guilty and unworthy of the same treatment for themselves.

Healing requires many things but your inner ally will not shine brightly if you don't show it the compassion to do so.

Courage and Strength

The last major character Dorothy meets on her journey is the lion, who very much wishes to be brave. He represents the need for courage and strength. No one doubts the bravery healthcare workers showed during the pandemic—except for themselves. While you showed courage and strength for others, at the end of the day, you often had none left for yourselves.

As a psychologist, I often have conversations with clients about the courage it takes to heal, whether from tragedy, trauma, crisis, grief, depression, anxiety or any other factor that affects the human condition. For those of you who now choose to embark upon your healing path to post-COVID recovery, the "lion" in you will be called upon in many ways—to acknowledge that healing needs to take place as well as to actually do the work to help you evolve beyond your weary state. While you've often heard your experience during the pandemic likened to that of a battle, you've already mustered the courage to keep it together even when you actually felt like falling apart. Napoleon Bonaparte, a military leader from the French Revolution said, "Courage isn't having the strength to go on—it is going on when you don't have the strength." When you are ready, the path will be waiting.

Why the Soul Matters
Be bold, take courage… and be strong of soul.
−Ovid

As healthcare professionals, you were taught to use your head to solve problems. While it is true that we need an education to practice in our particular fields, we need far more to heal ourselves. The healing process requires that we use all aspects of our inner self to not only fully heal, but also to transcend our previous human condition. We certainly need our head to help us understand how we got where we did and our hearts to have the compassion and tenderness to nurture and support ourselves along the way. Most important, we need our soul—the wisdom of our inner self—to inform us of what *we* individually need on our path to healing. Listening to and heeding the instructions of your inner ally is what will help you to fully and effectively navigate your healing journey.

Ironically, prior to the invention of "modern medicine", all healers were spiritual figures first. It was the priests, nuns, ministers, medicine men and shamans who cared for the sick. Even the first hospitals were housed in churches. As science progressed, we left the soul out of healing altogether. But even now, over ninety percent of those surveyed wish their medical practitioners would integrate spirituality into the treatment patients receive. Perhaps now is the perfect time to reacquaint you with your soul.

While healthcare practitioners need a protocol or procedure to heal them, it needs to be individually created to fit the soul that needs to be healed. Therefore, your healing path needs to be as unique as each soul that exists—it needs to fit *you* and *your* needs rather than meet the needs of others. Nothing else will do and nothing else will help you find your light again.

Aligning with your soul—your inner ally—on your path to healing will guarantee a much brighter outcome than a one-size-fits-all approach. Learning to listen and align with the needs of our soul gives us the most accurate awareness of who we are at a core level as well as provides the most direct line to the light at the end of our path. It offers the precision we need in order to release what no longer serves us while embracing and welcoming what will enhance our lives. In essence, our truth IS our radiance—our inner light. It is the wisdom that lights our path to both healing and to evolution.

Dorothy's quest down the golden path helped her realize that happiness wasn't actually outside of herself. She had to face the darkness of the storm and learn from her experiences along the way. She made it home with more knowledge, wisdom and understanding of why she faced the storm.

Your path to healing requires three basic things: A willingness to listen to your inner self telling you what you need, an understanding of how to rebuild and enhance your tree of life using the concepts you've learned about the Soul Health Model and a commitment to E.V.O.L.V.E. beyond the place you never knew existed.

You now have a chance to take what you've experienced to become the magnificent tree mentioned in Chapter One—more whole and even better than prior to the pandemic. You've explored the branches of health that need attention and you see how the soul plays an essential part. You now also have the necessary tools to rebuild your life, perhaps one that you couldn't see even prior to the arrival of COVID-19. For the first time, you may see that you deserve to live life fully and more brightly despite what you have experienced. Let your inner self lead the way.

Soul-Based Healing
Every man dies–Not every man really lives.
–WILLIAM ROSE WALLACE

The remaining chapters will help you create your healing path to post-COVID recovery. With the help of curiosity about creating a better future, compassion toward yourself along the way and courage to face the darkened branches, you will have no problem taking the action necessary to find your light. As someone who has been fully immersed in the challenges of the human condition throughout the pandemic, you have the right to discover, honor, claim and *live* more fully. Below are the steps to living through your soul to embark on your path to healing.

1. Listen within.

Throughout this book you have been encouraged to listen to your inner self to determine what you need—or don't need—to create a more fulfilling and "healed" life. Through learning about the *Three Questions of Discernment*, the E.V.O.L.V.E. "procedure" and the Soul Health Model, your picture of health likely came more clearly into view. In each chapter, you encountered several examples, exercises, and suggestions for assessing what needs attention. Although many healthcare professionals think they should be able to heal their own wounds, it might be helpful to enlist the expertise of others—a therapist or life coach—to assist. Keep in mind that most professionals aren't yet trained to do deeper work related to the soul. This book can guide you in listening from the core or essence of who you are.

2. *Hear* the message.

Our culture doesn't teach us to listen to our soul; instead, only our thoughts are valued in leading us through life. Have you often ignored or denied what your gut (the voice of your soul) was telling you only for life to go awry? Listening to oneself above others has been punished and dismissed as selfish or unimportant. Because our unique selves need different things to balance our tree of life, we have to remember that our path to healing will be equally distinctive. Hearing the messages from within will inform your path to a brighter day.

3. Interpret the message.

Our discontent or dis-ease indicates that we are not aligned with our soul, although we often choose to ignore these cues. As you learned about each branch of the Soul Health Model and explored the questionnaires, you likely felt something stir deep inside when you realized something was misaligned or amiss. Learning to notice these messages and the patterns for when your discontent arises will help you pay closer attention to how, when, and why your emotions or other discomforts get triggered. Simply notice the internal stirrings, then observe and learn from what they are trying to tell you. Then, you will be better able to align the branches of your tree.

4. Separate your tree from the forest around it.

Although we have others in our lives whom we need to consider, it is important to separate what is yours from what is theirs and "root" yourself with an understanding of what *your* soul uniquely wants and needs. You must distinguish your thoughts from others', separate your feelings from those of the people around you, and identify your ideas and beliefs from those that prevail in the world at large. In other words, you must learn to recognize that your soul is uniquely yours and yours alone. If you do not listen to it and honor it, no one else will—or can.

5. Prioritize the essence of who you are.

Many have been taught that it is selfish to act on their own needs and beliefs. To me, there is a huge difference between being selfish and living *for self*. Selfish people disregard others and have little or no concern for them or their needs. Living a life of soul health is entirely different. When we truly live through our soul, we act through the purity of our inner wisdom and our actions work for the alignment and purity of all others as well. For instance, when we assert ourselves with others, for the sake of our soul health, we educate another's soul. We demonstrate how to rise above self-interest alone. Saying yes to what another person wants when you know it will work against your soul health will only dishonor your own truth—*and* the soul of the other person, whether they realize it or not. You may not give the person what they want, but it may be what they need. Ironically, those who are selfish often perceive selfishness in others. On the other hand, actions that serve the soul—those that are *for self* rather than *selfish*—are generally well-received by those who likewise honor their inner ally.

Prioritizing your inner ally is of utmost importance in creating your healing path. Without this vital step, you will not be able to distinguish your tree of life within the vast forest.

6. Commit to evolution.

Comedian, Seth MacFarlane, said "Evolution doesn't care whether you believe in it or not, no more than gravity does." The concept of *evolving* beyond your previous state as part of healing is new to many. It is a gradual and slow process that takes you to a new and better form. Your healing path requires you to commit to *exploring* your circumstance, *envisioning* a brighter future, *observing* yourself along the way, *learning* what you can, *venturing* into something new and *elevating* yourself to a higher, but deeper place in your human condition. With soul health in mind, if you leave your tree as it currently stands, you will feel no better. You will remain in your dark forest, without an appreciation for your inner self. However, if you choose to live through your soul by understanding how to improve the many branches of soul health, you will also align with your inner self, which creates a luminous future. It is the only path to evolution.

Partnering with your inner self is the only way your tree of life can flourish—it is the only way we fully thrive and the only way our souls will grow. By investing the time and energy in exploring the branches of health that need work, then creating your "soul health plan", your healing path will quickly take form.

CHAPTER EIGHTEEN

THE SOUL'S PLAN

Healing is a matter of time, but it is sometimes
also a matter of opportunity.

—HIPPOCRATES

In the last chapter, I mentioned that it takes the wisdom of our head, heart *and* soul to truly heal. Jointly, they can do no wrong, but separately the former two aspects can lead us astray—especially on an essential path to healing. Individually, both our heads and hearts can lead us down the wrong path, but our inner truth—our gut reactions and "voice" of our soul—never do. The words you have read and the concepts you have learned are the tools you need to redesign your life for a brighter future. Now it is time to take the opportunity to put your thoughts into action.

This chapter provides the next steps on your healing path. You will review what you learned about your branches of health, take a more comprehensive and integrated look at your tree of life, and then create a systematic plan for how to move forward.

Step One

The questionnaires included in Chapters 7 through 16 helped you assess what needs attention in each of the ten branches of your soul health. Below, you will find a Soul Health Assessment, which will help you put it all together from the viewpoint of your soul. When you assess each branch from a soul-based level you will achieve a deeper understanding of your unique soul needs.

The Soul Health Assessment yields a numerical result that will show you which branches are most urgent to address. As you consider each statement, give it a rating from 1 (almost never) to 5 (almost always). The branches with the lowest total scores are the ones you need to work on first—they are the most in need of your attention. Assessing the health of these branches will get you started on your path to healing.

Evaluating your branches of soul health is not meant to overwhelm you. The process simply guides you to a brighter future. For that reason, no generalized numerical measure of ideal health is necessary, since you cannot compare your unique tree of life to any other. The numerical ranking system is simply a guide to a relatively objective understanding of where to start on your Soul Health Plan. The next chapter offers greater detail on how to create a plan for soul health.

Soul Health Assessment

Physical Health

1 2 3 4 5   I know that physical health is important to my overall soul health.

1 2 3 4 5   I feel healthy, vibrant, and strong at a deep level.

1 2 3 4 5   I understand what my soul tells me about my body.

1 2 3 4 5   I know how to care for my body at the soul level.

1 2 3 4 5   My physical health shows that I take good care of my inner self.

1 2 3 4 5   My soul is happy with how I treat my body.

1 2 3 4 5   My inner self informs me about my nutritional needs.

1 2 3 4 5   I eat only what creates a healthy body and a healthy soul.

1 2 3 4 5   I am deeply satisfied with my level of physical activity.

1 2 3 4 5   My levels of sleep and rest reflect a healthy soul.

1 2 3 4 5   I understand that ailments are often symptoms of an uneasy soul.

Total: _____

Psychological Health

1 2 3 4 5   My inner self feels at ease.

1 2 3 4 5   I know what I need to change in my emotional life.

1 2 3 4 5   My soul is reflected in my positive thoughts about myself.

1 2 3 4 5   I know and accept who I am at a deep level.

1 2 3 4 5   My inner self is open to joy and love.

1 2 3 4 5   My emotional boundaries align with the needs of my soul.

1 2 3 4 5   I allow the world to see who I am at a deep level.

1 2 3 4 5   My soul knows I take good care of my psychological health.

1 2 3 4 5   I am deeply at peace with myself.

1 2 3 4 5   I know my emotions are messages from my soul.

1 2 3 4 5   I am deeply satisfied with where I am in my life.

Total: _____

Social Health

1 2 3 4 5   I have enough social support to satisfy the needs of my soul.

1 2 3 4 5   I have only soulful relationships with others.

1 2 3 4 5   I recognize when a relationship is unhealthy for my soul.

1 2 3 4 5   My family is supportive of me at the soul level.

1 2 3 4 5   My friends are supportive of me at the soul level.

1 2 3 4 5   The people in my life are good for my soul.

1 2 3 4 5   I am deeply satisfied with the time I spend with others.

1 2 3 4 5   My inner self is filled rather than depleted by the people in my life.

1 2 3 4 5   I am at ease with the people in my life.

1 2 3 4 5   I am at ease in most social situations.

1 2 3 4 5   My life is filled with people who are healthy for my soul.

Total: _____

Interpersonal Health

1 2 3 4 5   I am deeply satisfied with the kinds of relationships I have.

1 2 3 4 5   My soul is satisfied with how others treat me.

1 2 3 4 5   The people in my life respect me at a deep level.

1 2 3 4 5   I communicate what I need from others to honor my soul.

1 2 3 4 5   I actively resolve conflict so that my soul can be at ease.

1 2 3 4 5   My inner self is safe with the people in my life.

1 2 3 4 5   The needs of my soul are honored by others in my life.

1 2 3 4 5   My relationships reflect the needs of my soul.

1 2 3 4 5   The people in my life understand me at a deep level.

1 2 3 4 5   My soul alerts me when others place conditions on our relationship.

1 2 3 4 5   I leave relationships that are not healthy for my soul.

Total: _____

Intellectual/Occupational Health

1 2 3 4 5   I am deeply satisfied by my occupational/intellectual efforts.

1 2 3 4 5   I only pursue intellectual challenges that are right for my soul.

1 2 3 4 5   I solve occupational problems based on what my inner self needs.

1 2 3 4 5   I am challenged, not bored, by my life overall.

1 2 3 4 5   My work feeds my soul.

1 2 3 4 5   My work is aligned with what I truly want in life.

1 2 3 4 5   My outlook is generally positive.

1 2 3 4 5   I see intellectual challenges as opportunities for my soul to grow.

1 2 3 4 5   My inner self embraces change rather than fears it.

1 2 3 4 5   My soul tells me when to take a break from intellectual work.

1 2 3 4 5   I know that my outlook on life affects the health of my soul.

Total: _____

Environmental Health

1 2 3 4 5   My home environment reflects the needs of my soul.

1 2 3 4 5   I know that my personal choices affect the world around me.

1 2 3 4 5   My inner self feels connected to the natural environment.

1 2 3 4 5   My respect for the earth is reflected in my actions.

1 2 3 4 5   I actively create a personal environment that supports inner peace.

1 2 3 4 5   My belongings help me to feel at peace.

1 2 3 4 5   I honor the earth as I would my own soul.

1 2 3 4 5   I know my personal environment mirrors the health of my soul.

1 2 3 4 5   My soul feels at ease in my home environment.

1 2 3 4 5   My soul feels at ease in my work environment.

1 2 3 4 5   My environment reflects my core beliefs.

Total: _____

Financial Health

1 2 3 4 5   I am at peace with my current financial situation.

1 2 3 4 5   I am at peace with how I spend money.

1 2 3 4 5   I make financial decisions based on what my soul needs.

1 2 3 4 5   My soul is comfortable with how I save money.

1 2 3 4 5   My purchases are more need-based than frivolous.

1 2 3 4 5   I feel grounded when I make most purchases.

1 2 3 4 5   My inner self is at ease with my level of debt.

1 2 3 4 5   My soul is at ease with my financial future.

1 2 3 4 5   I know when a purchase feels wrong to my soul.

1 2 3 4 5   My soul is at ease when I think about money.

1 2 3 4 5   My soul knows I take care of my finances.

Total: _____

Sexual Health

1 2 3 4 5   My sex life satisfies my soul.

1 2 3 4 5   I am at peace with my sexuality.

1 2 3 4 5   I only engage in soulful sex.

1 2 3 4 5   I am at peace with my sexual interests and needs.

1 2 3 4 5   I only engage in sex with soulful partners.

1 2 3 4 5   I am at ease with my sexual past.

1 2 3 4 5   My soul feels safe when I engage in sex.

1 2 3 4 5   I am able to enjoy sex.

1 2 3 4 5   My soul feels at ease when I think about sex.

1 2 3 4 5   I know that soulful sex requires a mutual decision.

1 2 3 4 5   After having sex, I never feel my soul has been dishonored.

Total: _____

Spiritual Health

1 2 3 4 5   I look for the deeper meaning of life's events.

1 2 3 4 5   I actively practice my spirituality.

1 2 3 4 5   My soul is at peace with my spiritual beliefs and practices.

1 2 3 4 5   My spirituality fills my soul.

1 2 3 4 5   My soul tells me when it needs spiritual attention.

1 2 3 4 5   I can share my spiritual beliefs with the people in my life.

1 2 3 4 5   My spirituality is important to the health of my soul.

1 2 3 4 5   I actively seek spiritual activities in order to grow.

1 2 3 4 5   I know that my spirituality helps my soul to evolve.

1 2 3 4 5   Quiet time helps me hear my soul more clearly.

1 2 3 4 5   I know what my soul needs to feel spiritually satisfied.

Total: _____

Recreational Health

1 2 3 4 5   My life is filled with joyful activities.

1 2 3 4 5   My soul is satisfied with the fun in my life.

1 2 3 4 5   My soul is satisfied with the leisure in my life.

1 2 3 4 5   I would describe my soul as joyful.

1 2 3 4 5   I actively create fun to feed my soul.

1 2 3 4 5   I actively create leisure to restore my soul.

1 2 3 4 5   My soul tells me when I need more fun and leisure in life.

1 2 3 4 5   I know what is fun to me.

1 2 3 4 5   I know what restores my soul.

1 2 3 4 5   My soul is at peace with what I do for fun.
1 2 3 4 5   I know that fun and leisure are important to soul health.

Total: _____

Step Two

Now that you have completed the Soul Health Assessment, list below the three branches of soul health that had the lowest scores in ascending order:

(lowest score) _____
(second lowest score) _____
(third lowest score) _____

Take a minute to decide if these are the branches that you *deeply* feel need the most attention or whether other branches feel like higher priorities given your current situation. If you need to reorganize your branches, do so, since your inner self may be guiding you to the areas in most urgent need of help. Your gut (soul) reaction will tell you whether you have prioritized these appropriately.

Step Three

Before you go on to create your Soul Health Plan, it is important to have a clear vision of the level of radiant living you want to achieve. I encourage you to find quiet, uninterrupted time to envision how you would like your overall health to be in one year. Try to visualize in detail how you want your life to look and feel in each of the branches of your soul health when you have reached your optimal level of radiant living.

Now take some time to write down this vision to include:

1. How your soul health would feel in one year.

2. What would be different about *you* as a result?

3. What would be different about your life?

4. How much more life or radiance you would experience.

5. How much more fulfilled you would be.

6. How working on self-compassion would facilitate your journey to soul health.

Take as much time as necessary exploring your thoughts about your vision of soul health.

As you have become aware through the E.V.O.L.V.E. protocol, envisioning a brighter and more fulfilling future is an essential part of your path to healing. The clearer and more detailed your vision the more easily you will achieve it. Of course, it is important to be realistic about what you can achieve in a year, but remember that your experiences during the pandemic might have deepened your understanding about what you really need to fulfill you at a soul level.

Soul Health Plan

Step Four

Now, you will begin to improve your health on each of the branches you identified as being in need of work. Keep in mind that the interrelationship among the branches is synergistic: that is, the effect of working on individual branches affects the whole structure. Although you will create a plan to work on each separate branch, you will positively affect the other branches and your entire tree of life.

In the process, you will more specifically identify within each branch: 1) what needs to be cleaned out or eliminated, and 2) what needs to be filled up or fortified. You can use the *Three Questions of Discernment* discussed throughout this book to help you decide what must stay and what must go. Remember, it is often necessary to make room for positive growth by removing obstacles that block the way to soul health. Be as honest and specific with yourself as you can, using your inner self to guide you. Keep in mind, we only achieve what we can identify specifically, so avoid generalized answers and allow your soul to guide you in the work that needs to be done to enhance your tree of life. Use a journal, notebook, or the spaces in this book to complete the following outline for the three branches you identified needing work:

Priority Branch # 1 _____

What needs to be *eliminated* from this branch of soul health?

1. _____

   _____

2. _____

   _____

3. _____

   _____

4. _____

   _____

What steps must *you* take in order to clean out this branch?

1. _____

   _____

2. _____

_____

3. _____

_____

4. _____

_____

What needs to be *fortified or filled up* in this branch of soul health?

1. _____

_____

2. _____

_____

3. _____

_____

4. _____

_____

What steps must *you* take in order to fill up this branch?

1. _____

_____

2. _____

_____

3. _____

_____

4. _____

_____

Priority Branch # 2 _____

What needs to be *eliminated* from this branch of soul health?

1. _____

_____

2. _____

_____

3. _____

_____

4. _____

_____

What steps must *you* take in order to clean out this branch?

1. _____

_____

2. _____

_____

3. _____

_____

4. _____

_____

What needs to be *fortified or filled up* in this branch of soul health?

1. _____

_____

2. _____

_____

3. _____

_____

4. _____

_____

What steps must *you* take in order to fill up this branch?

1. _____

_____

2. _____

_____

3. _____

_____

4. _____

_____

Priority Branch # 3 _____

What needs to be *eliminated* from this branch of soul health?

1. _____

_____

2. _____

_____

3. _____

_____

4. _____

_____

What steps must *you* take in order to clean out this branch?

1. _____

_____

2. _____

_____

3. _____

_____

4. _____

_____

What needs to be *fortified or filled up* in this branch of soul health?

1. _____

_____

2. _____

_____

3. _____

_____

4. _____

_____

What steps must *you* take in order to fill up this branch?

1. _____

_____

2. _____

_____

3. _____

_____

4. _____

_____

Step Five

Now that you have completed this process, you have identified at least some steps you need to take to create your path to healing. It is common to hesitate on following through with some of the actions identified above. To evolve beyond any blockages, ask yourself the following questions (and remember it is useful to write your responses down as you go, because this will help you reach a deeper soul level):

- What obstacles do I see in following through with any actions I need to take?
- What will it take for me to remain conscious of my goals?
- How do I sabotage my own growth and evolution?
- What would I regret more—growing or not growing?
- What assistance do I need in my process of reaching optimal soul health?

+ How willing am I to seek and make use of this help?
+ What needs to happen before I can follow through and honor my soul?
+ In what ways do I need to continue to work on self-love or self-compassion to ensure radiant health?

Our human condition—the basis of our fears and flaws—is always a factor when we try to change something in our lives. Unexpected shifts in our lives—much like your experiences during the pandemic—also affect our ability to follow through with our plans. Once you overcome your mental and emotional roadblocks, you can embark on your healing path and reach a much brighter future.

Step Six

Listening to and taking action based on what your inner self tells you is the most important and often most difficult part of reaching soul health.

Now that you have completed the first five steps, it is time to set some goals for your one-year mark. Keep in mind that evolution is a process and that it takes conscious effort on your part. You may cycle back to old patterns, habits and behaviors, but this is also part of evolution.

Consider the following:

+ Do you do better with daily, weekly, or monthly goals?
+ Do you need someone or something to keep you accountable?
+ How do you best monitor your progress (even if you don't like doing it)?
+ How will you know if you are getting off track?
+ How will you know when you need help to reach your goals?

Step Six entails actually setting and acting on your goals. Only you and your deepest self knows when it is time to move forward. Consider the following method of identifying your goals:

+ What does your gut (soul) say about setting goals for soul health?

+ How will your inner self tell you when you aren't working for its benefit?

+ What sort of gut (soul) reaction will tell you when you are off track?

Now, take some time to plan whatever feels right to you in your commitment to achieve your vision of soul health in the next twelve months. Write this down so that you can revisit it at any time, as we all need reminders for how to get to where our inner truth wants us to be. I encourage weekly exploration of your progress since this is helpful in assessing whether you are moving in the direction of soul health. I have also found that it is helpful to review your progress every two or three months. Looking back over your progress shows you that you are actually achieving goals along the path. Affirming your progress is a necessary part of growth and it helps you decide on next steps toward evolution.

Once you have completed the steps in this chapter, you are likely to continue creating your radiant health—your nicely balanced tree of life. The next chapter emphasizes the importance of becoming a steward of your soul as you proceed.

CHAPTER NINETEEN

STEWARDSHIP TO OUR SOUL AND OTHERS'

When we try to pick out anything by itself,
we find it hitched to everything else in the Universe.
—JOHN MUIR

Everything and everyone is connected. The pandemic clearly proved that not only are we all in this human condition together, but we all affect it for better or worse. Throughout my interviews with healthcare providers for this book, I heard story after story about how medical teams came together to try to fix a world that was falling apart. I heard the frustration of practitioners who couldn't convince their patients to care for themselves and others by first wearing masks, then by getting the vaccine. I heard about pervasive discord between family members, friends and partners whose views differed about whether the virus was really a "thing". I also heard providers tell stories about shared tender experiences with coworkers who cheered each other on regardless of the exhaustion and loss they experienced themselves. Never in our lifetime was it so obvious that each person's actions were hitched to each and every other's, whether for good or bad. But remember, out of darkness always comes light.

The ebb and flow of forestation tells a story similar to humanity. I graduated from high school just three days before Yellowstone National Park caught fire on June 14, 1988. At the time, it was the worst fire in U.S. history, burning nearly 800,000 acres—36% total acreage of the park. Humans started nine fires and forty-two were ignited from lightning strikes—indicating that both people and Mother Nature together caused the destruction. The world's first national park, made official by Ulysses S. Grant in 1872, was also the first to go up in flames. Common policy was to allow fires to burn themselves out naturally, something even President Ronald Reagan didn't know at the time. This brought much controversy since the country's original natural landmark was slowly being destroyed. However, when the fires continued to spread even five weeks later, the "let it burn" rule was dropped and nearly 10,000 firefighters—the largest company in history—came together to fight the battle. It took over five months for the final embers to go out. Millions of trees and thousands of animals perished in the historical event, something that both literally and figuratively scarred both our land and nation.

I visited Yellowstone for the first time in 2011, twenty-three years after the historic event. As I drove through the vast expanse of the park, I saw rolling hills of lush lodgepole pines, the trees most affected by the fire. As far as I could see, millions of new growth trees—all taller than I—covered the rolling hills. What few knew about these pines is that their seeds, tucked tightly in the cones they produced, could only be released when subjected to the heat of fire. Only when tragedy struck could a new forest emerge and thrive.

We don't yet know what good will come from the coronavirus pandemic. We also don't know how long the "embers" will burn—the lasting effect of this multi-layered historical occasion. But what we do know is that, with care, healing will take place over time. Essayist, Ralph Waldo Emerson said, "Every spirit builds itself a house, and beyond its house, a world, and beyond its world, a heaven. Know then that world exists for you." Although you, our healthcare workers have always been good stewards to those you served, it is now time to become stewards to yourselves—stewards to your own inner light. This service to yourself will allow you to heal, emerge as an evolved soul and thrive as you enter into a new phase of life.

Tending to Your Tree of Life

A weed is a plant that has mastered every survival skill
except for learning how to grow in rows.
–Doug Larson

Stewardship usually means that we have taken on the responsibility of caring for something other than ourselves—usually an organization or property. However, we also have a personal responsibility to care for and manage our own lives. The challenge, particularly for professional caregivers, is that we often don't know how to take care of ourselves, let alone master the skills that are essential in doing so. While someone who is called a Master Gardener is trained in the art and science of tending to the environment, training in the art and science of self—or soul care—often eludes healthcare workers. If this was the case prior to the pandemic, it is more important than ever to learn to become a steward of your tree of life now, both to create and embark on your healing path and to learn how to maintain your newfound light once your path is fully in place.

Throughout this book, you were encouraged to apply the *Three Questions of Discernment* to help you assess whether something enhanced or diminished your life. Discernment is an acquired skill, neither something we are taught early in life nor something that is encouraged by those who want you to take care of them instead. However, as part of the healer's path, your willingness to discern the needs of your inner self is really the only sustainable method to heal from your experience of the pandemic. By learning how to sense what is misaligned and what needs to be done to correct it, you will clear the way to a new tomorrow and fortify your life so you can experience optimal health.

Stewardship of your soul's garden—your truest needs—requires a commitment to lovingly and consciously attend to your needs at all times, regardless of your circumstances. In the case of healthcare workers who need to heal from the circumstances of COVID-19, it means promising your inner self that you will listen and respond to what will truly align your life so that you can also go on to care for others. It has become cliché to say that you have to take care of yourself before you can take care of others, but from your experiences of the pandemic you likely understand why this is so true.

Discernment is an internal, proactive process that prepares you to take external action so you can become a better steward to your inner self and experience optimal health. Your healing path will only provide the quality and extent of results you desire when you are willing to put your discernment into action. The Soul Health Model provides the framework for understanding which aspects of your human condition need work in order to rebalance your life and experience "radiant" health. The *Three Questions of Discernment* help you to make decisions about what needs to be cleaned out and/or added to enrich each branch of health as well as to the overall health of your soul—the essence of who *you* are. Finally, the E.V.O.L.V.E. protocol helps you put your thoughts into action. Here's how you put it all together:

1. *Examine* your branches of health on the Soul Health Model by using the *Three Questions of Discernment*. Make sure you also explore the needs of your inner self—your soul—as a whole.

2. *Envision* how each branch or area of your life would feel and look once it is balanced. Do the same for your overall soul health.

3. *Observe* your thoughts, feelings and actions as you take steps to change your life. This level of consciousness allows you to catch yourself when you are getting off track as well as keep you focused on the light at the end.

4. **Learn** about yourself along your journey. Remember, evolution happens slowly and doesn't occur in a straight line. Your path to healing will provide many opportunities for growth.

5. **Venture** into a new you. As you embark on your healing journey, your perspective will change. Your outlook will become brighter and you will become both empowered and energized to continue your growth.

6. **Elevate** yourself to new heights. Let the image of your brightening inner light guide you as you move beyond familiar discomfort.

Mastering the challenges of the human condition is a life-long process. If given the tools, you can become a master of tending to your soul's garden.

Brightening Your Inner Light

The morning steals upon the night, melting the darkness.
–William Shakespeare

Nature guarantees two things will happen every day—the sun will rise and it will set. Darkness will always be followed by light. Although it might be difficult to see and experience your own light following the challenges you've faced as a healthcare worker during the coronavirus pandemic, you now have more tools to brighten your way.

Our soul's most natural state is that of joy and contentment. Only when something dims our view or darkens our path do we feel anything else. When our experiences of the human condition pile up, our light—our birthright of bliss—can get buried beneath. As you read this book, you will likely see some glimpses of what life could be like once you clear your path and enrich your existence. You may have also questioned whether it was possible to actually step fully out of the darkness to experience a new light—possibly one you never even knew existed. Playwright, Mehmet Murat Ildan said, "Every morning is a revolution against the darkness." Now, it is up to you to reclaim your light beyond those darkened days.

It seems important to revisit the idea of self-love and compassion as you embark on your journey. Since writing edition one of my first book, *Soul Health: Aligning with Spirit for Radiant Living* in which I first describe The Soul Health Model, the idea of "love consciousness" has exploded. Numerous authors and researchers have attempted to explain why behavior change is so hard—why we resist, regardless of our desire to experience a more favorable outcome. Researchers have studied everything from personality characteristics, coping styles, differences in willpower, levels of resiliency, brain activity, biological factors and even spiritual and religious beliefs related to change. None have yet to solve the problem.

I had an epiphany several years ago about why people resist evolution. It came in an ironic way—the answer arose as I reflected upon the inevitability of death. This "ah ha" moment changed everything about how I lived my own life as well as how I helped others live theirs.

Shortly after publishing the first edition of Soul Health, my elderly mother's health began to fail. For nearly six years, I not only watched her health decline, I also observed how she perceived and led her life. This made me reflect back on my father's death when I was twenty-one and also on how he led his life since an accident he had when I was just nine. Neither of my parents took good care of themselves and both of them seemed to have many regrets.

I began to contemplate the deeper question behind why we seem to repeat the same negative patterns over and over again. I explored the reasons at the core of why clients, friends, colleagues and anyone else—including me—stumble throughout life. Low self-esteem, confidence issues, body image, lack of assertiveness, insecurities, difficulty kicking addictions, challenges with eating disorders, relationship concerns, regret, guilt, inability to overcome fear and so on all ran through my brain. I wanted to know what was behind all of our struggles within the human condition.

The answer came to me one morning as I finished breakfast. I suddenly realized that the primary factor behind every bit of resistance to changing, healing or evolving was a lack of self-love. Because the events of the human condition can take a toll on our well-being, our tree of life can slowly deteriorate if left unattended and unloved. As the events of the human condition unfold, we are often less and less able to maintain life balance and the "wholeness" of our souls. Without love of self, our ability to acknowledge and repair our tree of life is compromised, which leaves both our human condition and soul to suffer. Our light dims and we have a hard time reigniting the light. As a result, we fail to move forward to create our much desired and radiant life.

At the core of all desires, what people want most is to be loved, accepted and nurtured. Through my observations about death and the human condition in general, it is now undeniable that each and every concern, stressor, challenge or conundrum we experience stems from a lack of self-love and compassion. As healthcare providers, you might go to great lengths to make others feel cared for, but like most other humans, you likely don't strive to do this for yourself.

At the core of soul health is self-love. Without self-compassion no one can sustain permanent change and no one will evolve beyond their own concerns. We have to love ourselves enough to take the steps necessary to change. Therefore, without self-love we will not fully embark on our healing path—we won't practice discernment and we won't follow through to E.V.O.L.V.E.

Although many have come to believe that self-love is wrong or even sinful, without this affection toward oneself, no one would ever heal. Your healing path would continue to be darkened and you would never find your way back to the joy and contentment your soul deserves. After nearly thirty-four years of working to help others heal, I am convinced that people are afraid to shine their inner light and more comfortable keeping it dim. This is because many are used to feeling so diminished by life that they don't take the steps to find and claim the light that is their own.

Self-love is required to heal. Many branches of your human condition were likely diminished or altered as a result of the pandemic. Your success in restoring each one depends on how much you practice self-love and compassion on your path to healing. While an understanding of how your soul—the deepest essence of who you are—is essential in creating an image of your healing path, it is the practice of self-love that will help you actually take action to create your most radiant life. As you embark on your healing journey, you will simultaneously learn to love yourself as well. Honoring the needs of your soul and loving yourself enough to heal guarantee you a more radiant life.

Actress and comedian, Lucille Ball said, "Love yourself first and everything else falls into line." The term "soul health" didn't exist while she was alive, but she clearly understood that life lined up when self-love was part of your life's plan. You cannot be a good steward to your soul and your overall health if you don't include love for self as a key element of the process.

Attaining soul health takes time. Committing to becoming a good steward requires periodic exploration of what you can do to stay aware of your daily needs. While some branches might remain evened out or balanced, others might need more attention from time to time depending on life events. The following set of questions could serve as a daily reminder of your ongoing quest for a more balanced life.

Guide to Daily Soul Health

Use the following questions for daily attention to your Healing Path.

- How has my soul thrived today?
- How has my inner self struggled today?
- Which branch or branches needed the most attention today?
- What did I do today to rebalance or restore this branch (or these branches)?
- What can I do tomorrow that will prevent an imbalance of my soul health the next day?
- How can I work on self-love today to enhance my soul health?

CHAPTER TWENTY

MAINTAINING YOUR SOUL'S FIRE

The most powerful weapon on earth is the human soul on fire.
—FERDINAND FOCH

Finding, nurturing and maintaining your inner light is the foundation of the healer's path. No matter where you are in your healing process, you know it is just that—a process. By now, you realize that if you really want to experience optimal health—or a radiant life—there are many branches of your well-being that must be examined to guarantee a brighter future.

The human condition tossed us quite a jumbled mess in bringing COVID-19 into our lives. More than anyone, you—our healthcare workers, absorbed the multi-layered impact of the pandemic, which means that you also need a dynamic method of realigning your life. The Soul Health Model provides the blueprint to explore, rebalance and restore your life. Along with this blueprint, the *Three Questions of Discernment* and the E.V.O.L.V.E. protocol will help to construct the path that will allow you to move beyond the darkness. Your dark night of the soul will soon be behind you and the concepts you learned about in this book will light the way on your path to healing.

The Well-Lit Tunnel

Seems like the light at the end of the tunnel may be you.
—Steven Tyler, Aerosmith

As I mentioned early in this book, one of my own dark nights happened at the end of graduate school. My education was hard enough, but I also had other "human" stressors that added to the pile—an unhealthy marriage, a family member who suffered a serious mental health crisis, and ongoing grief from the death of my father to name a few. During my doctoral program, I attended a national conference in Toronto, Canada then swung over to Niagara Falls to take in the sights before heading home. Behind the powerful waterfall is a tunnel that leads to an arch-shaped "window" where you can view the force of the rapidly cascading waters. From there, you can feel and hear the immense energy of the natural feature.

As I admired the strength of the waters, I also realized that the image represented "the light at the end". While the tunnel itself was dark, the light coming through the waters that fell beyond the arched frame illuminated the far end of the passageway. Somehow from that point on, I knew I would make it through that difficult time. I snapped a picture of that well-lit tunnel, seeing the bright light even behind the thick curtain of the waterfall. When I returned from the trip, I posted the picture above my desk and every time I wondered how I would make it through the next challenge, I used the metaphor behind the image as a reminder that light was just in front of me. I just had to find it and keep it in view.

Once found, your soul's light—its fire—can never be extinguished. The essence of who we are sustains us, even when we think our light will go out completely. But as you come to understand and embrace the concept of *soul health*, you will realize that it is your inner wisdom that informs you on your healing journey. You just need the structure—The Soul Health Model—and the method—the E.V.O.L.V.E. protocol to get you to your destination.

You are the light at the end of the tunnel.

Virtues of Your Healing Path

To plant trees is to give body and life to one's dreams of a better world.
–Russell Page

Evolution is an ongoing and often indirect process. The circumstances of the human condition often derail our path to wholeness and the coronavirus pandemic has thoroughly proven this. Because, in my mind, healing is not enough, your willingness to grow beyond your experiences guarantees that you will create and claim a better life. This requires us to appreciate several virtues along the healing path:

Self-Compassion—Having compassion toward ourselves may be difficult, especially as a healthcare provider who is more inclined to show compassion to others. Nurturing ourselves through the challenges of the human condition allows us to heal and grow more quickly and enter a state conducive to attaining optimal health—soul health.

Patience—Healing takes time and evolution never feels like it happens fast enough. Being patient with ourselves and our experience of the human condition is often the biggest challenge to our evolution. Just as the first fish that decided to stay on land took many dips back into the water before it decided to evolve, you will also eventually find higher ground.

Honesty—"To thine own self be true." Soul health is all about listening to and acting upon our inner wisdom. This level of health is unattainable without self-honesty. The Soul Health Model represents all aspects of the human condition that must be aligned before we can reach radiant living. Finding our light requires us to be honest about what we need and don't need for the health of every branch in our tree of life.

Courage—Change requires courage. We may experience many forms of trauma, misalignment, and tragedy as part of our human condition, but examining what needs work, envisioning a better tomorrow, observing our experiences, learning about ourselves, venturing into new levels of living life and elevating ourselves above our previously known ways can show us how brave we really are.

Commitment—While change takes courage, evolution takes commitment. Because achieving soul health is a process, paying unfailing attention to our inner ally requires a life-long commitment. Once you find your light, you won't want to lose it.

Diligence—Maintaining growth is an ongoing challenge, but in staying on top of your evolution, your soul rewards you many times over. The ultimate payout is optimal health.

Perseverance—Navigating "the good, the bad and the ugly" of the human condition is easier when we keep a steady focus on the light we will find at the end. Once you realize that soul health is not only possible but also yours to claim, your healing path will feel more like an investment than a burden.

Creativity—Surviving the human condition requires commitment and dedication. Thriving within it requires creative thinking. As you creatively explore how to rebalance the branches of your tree of life, you will awaken the inner light that will guide you on your path to optimal health.

Humor —I don't know anyone who heals without humor playing a part. Laughter dislodges us from the darkness of the human condition and elevates us above our challenges. Finding ways to tap into our soul's most natural state—joy and contentment—facilitates our healing process.

The Magnificent Tree of Life

Whenever you are creating beauty around you,
you are restoring your own soul.
—Alice Walker

When I first began the journey of writing the Healer's Path, I had no idea how much my life would change. As a healthcare provider, I too, was mentally exhausted by circumstances I couldn't control, disillusioned and baffled by how people acted, frustrated by the state of the world and burned out from working long hours. I was somewhat disengaged from my own tree of life and questioned whether I could make a difference during the dark night of the world's soul. Although hesitant to start the process, I soon became energized and even excited to meet and interview healthcare workers from around the United States. Shortly after, some from Canada also offered their observations. While the pandemic has yet to come to a complete end, I see my own light shining more brightly and I hope the path presented in this book will help you find yours as well.

Healing is one thing. Evolving beyond where we began is a whole other story—one that provides a much brighter outcome. The concept of soul health may have once been foreign to you, but now, I hope you understand that the essence of who you are—your soul—is the most important part of your healing journey. Without a conscious awareness of the essential nature of your soul, you would continue to stumble through the events of the human condition. But in learning to acknowledge and honor the needs of your soul, you are guaranteed to find more optimal health and lead a much more fulfilling life.

It might seem dramatic to say, but I often tell clients and workshop participants that our soul will be our salvation. What I mean by this is that the essence of who we are holds all the wisdom we need in order to live a better life—we just have to learn to acknowledge and listen to it. Once this happens, we can rely on it to guide every decision and action and in doing so we inevitably find ourselves on a brighter path.

When we let our soul light the way, the darkness loses its power and can never again dim our way.

Your light awaits you on your healing path. It is time to heal. It is time to evolve above and beyond the darkened days.

POSTSCRIPT

I finished the first draft of The Healer's Path seven months after starting the interview process with healthcare providers. Just in that short amount of time, many things had changed. Vaccines arrived on the scene, along with much controversy. Several new variants of the virus emerged, one of which—the Delta variant—wreaked havoc all over again, often in parts of the country that had already been hard hit. Many medical workers left or lost their jobs when they decided not to get the vaccine. Staff shortages added even more stress to an already strained healthcare system. Hostility increased when providers asked patients whether or not they had received the vaccine—something these professionals were required to do as part of their "helping" jobs. Even more people got sick and many more died.

Throughout my time writing, I was struck by the sociological impact the virus—a very physical condition—took on the rest of how the human condition works. When I started writing the book, I already knew that no branch of the human condition—as illustrated in the Soul Health Model—had been left untouched. As my world became immersed in the news, statistics, articles and personal accounts of the pandemic, it was clear that the world was changing in many deep and pervasive ways.

One of the practitioners I interviewed early in the process said that he had read a book about the 1918 pandemic to help him understand how these things go. The book is called *Pale Rider: The Spanish Flu of 1918 and How it Changed the World*, written by Laura Spinney, a medical historian. Also curious, I ordered the book and started reading it while on the first trip I had taken in over twenty months—my "carrot at the end" to help me complete The Healer's Path.

In reading the book, I was fascinated as much as disillusioned. I was captivated with how she wrote about both the reality behind a pandemic—the scientific truths about how they emerge and spread and the myth—what people believe or want to believe according to their motives, levels of understanding and general consciousness. It appears that not much has changed over the last hundred years. People are acting just about the same as they did a century before.

What has changed is that the population has grown by over seven billion people in just one hundred years. That number seems biologically impossible, but is scientifically true.

As a person who writes about the evolution of the human condition and the soul, it took me a while to get past the fact that much looks the same as it did at the beginning of the last century. When you think about all of the technological advances that have occurred in that time, you would think that humans, themselves, would have evolved at a similarly rapid pace. But as a whole, we haven't.

With seven billion more people on the planet than during the last full pandemic, there are more souls than we can keep up with in evolutionary terms. So while knowledge is power, wisdom is still necessary in order to evolve. We have a long way to go.

My "carrot at the end" trip was appropriately organized to visit the Redwood National and State parks in California. I'd seen these amazing trees briefly twice before but wanted to go enjoy the beauty and solitude of the ancient and giant forests to revitalize from my own time in lockdown, a continued busy therapy schedule and of course from writing this book. I spent six days hiking through the groves, often not seeing another soul throughout my entire journey. As I walked among those giants, their own "wounds" were more than apparent through the huge burls on their trunks, fire scars that blemished their roots and bark, hollowed centers indicating lightning strikes that could have been fatal and the debris that was scattered around their bases. What I had just spent five months writing about was visible before me in the language and image of the trees.

These groves are thousands of years old. They have seen fires, lightning strikes and other devastation many times and they will see it all again. In fact, as I traveled, I had to drive many miles out of the way just to get to the parks because most of north-central California was overtaken with enormous forest fires. Shortly after I returned home, fires broke out near Sequoia National Park, where "General Sherman", the current tallest and oldest redwood tree lives (275 feet tall and an estimated 2700 years old). The fires had encroached to just a few miles away from where it stands and the base had been wrapped with fire retardant materials in an attempt to save this natural American icon. The forestry "healthcare workers" experienced their own frantic battle to save this ancient soul.

Challenges will happen again. They too shall pass. Now, you hopefully have the tools and procedures to create an easier route on your path to healing—and growing beyond—where you are today.

Several months after I interviewed the family physician leader I mentioned a few times in this book, he sent a message to tell me that he now thinks of trees very differently. He said, "Each time I see a tree, I wonder what human is experiencing or has experienced that kind of tree trunk, the branches, the shapes and curves as they reach toward the light, grow, become injured, recover and heal." He updated me on his life, having made many changes to realign his own tree of life. The gift of his message affirmed the intention of this book—that the journey to the light beyond the darkness might be difficult, but given the right tools the path becomes a guarantee to a brighter and more fulfilling future.

As healthcare providers, the essence of who you are has been changed throughout the events of the pandemic, which likely added to the many layers of the human condition that might have already dimmed your view. By taking an active and "evolutionary" stance to your healing, you will no doubt become a magnificent tree.

Together, we can become a beautiful and vibrant forest.

REFERENCES

Chapter One

American Psychological Association. 2021. 1 in 4 Essential Workers (25%) Diagnosed with Mental Health Disorder Since Start of Pandemic. Accessed April 2021. https://www.apa.org/news/press/releases/2021/03/march-essential-workers.

American Psychological Association. 2020. Stress in America 2020. Accessed April 2020. https://www.apa.org/news/press/releases/stress/2020/report-october.

Census Bureau's County Business Patterns. 2018. Healthcare still the largest United States Employer. Accessed October 2020. https://www.census.gov/library/stories/2020/10/health-care-still-largest-united-states-employer.html.

Kelly, K. 2018. Soul Health: Aligning With Spirit for Radiant Living, Second Revised Edition. North Carolina: Soul Health Press.

Maunder, RG, Lancee, WJ, Balderson, KE et. all. 2006. Long-term psychological and occupational effects of providing hospital healthcare during SARS outbreak. Emergency Infectious Disease. 12: 1924-1932.

Moss, M, Good, VS, Gozal, D, Kleinpell, R & Sessler, CN. 2016. A critical care societies collaborative statement: Burnout syndrome in critical care health-care professionals. A call for action. American Journal of Respiratory Critical Care Medicine. 194: 106-113.

Pinho-Gomes, AC, Peters, S, Thompson, K et al. 2020. Where are the women? Gender inequalities in COVID-19 research authorship. British Medical Journal Global Health. 1-4.

United States Census Bureau. 2021. Census Bureau's 2018 County Business Patterns Provide Data on Over 1,200 Industries. Accessed January 2021. https://bpspsychub.onlinelibrary wiley.com/doi/abs/10.1111/bjc.12147.

Wohlleben, Peter. 2016. The Hidden Life of Trees: What They Feel, How They Communicate Discoveries from a Secret World. Greystone Books.

Chapter Three
American Institute of Stress. 2019. "The Holmes-Rahe Stress Inventory." Accessed March 2021. https://www.stress.org/holmes-rahe-stress-inventory.

American Journal of Medicine. 2019. Oath to Self-Care and Well-Being. Accessed March 2021. https://www.amjmed.com/article/S0002-9343.

American Psychological Association. 2009. An Action Plan for Self-Care. Accessed March 2021. https://www.apaservices.org/practice/good-practice/spring09-selfcare.pdf.

American Psychological Association. 2021. Self-Care Advice for Health-Care Providers During COVID-19. Accessed April 2021. https://www.apaservices.org/practice/ce-self-care/health-providers-covid-19.

EProvide. 2019. Stress Vulnerability Scale (SVS). Accessed April 2021. https://eprovide.mapi-trust.org/Instruments/stress-vulnerability-scale.

Forbes. 2016. Healing the Healer: Why Physicians and Medical Professionals Must Practice Self-Care. Accessed March 2021. https://www.forbes.com/sites/jeenacho/2016/03/30healing-the-healer-why-physicians-and-medical-professionals-must-practice-self-care/?sh=2957fe52797a.

Healthcare Toolbox. 2021. Self Care and Secondary Trauma for Providers. Accessed March 2021. https://healthcaretoolbox.org/self-care-for-provider.

Holmes, T. H. & Rahe, R. H. 1967. The social readjustment rating scale. Journal of Psychosomatic Research, 11(2), 213-218.

Kelly, K. 2019. The Recipe for Radiance: Mastering the Art and Soul of Self-Care. North Carolina: Soul Health Press.

Madrigal, I.P. & Smith, P. 2020. Stress, compassion fatigue and burnout handling in veterinary practice. Edra Publishers.

Mental Health First Aid. 2020. Healthcare, Mental Health First Aid, News, Self-Care. Accessed April 2021. https://www.mentalhealthfirstaid.org/2020/04/self-care-tips-for-health-care-workers/.

Merrit-Hawkins. 2021. The Importance of Self-Care for Healthcare Professionals during COVID-19. Accessed March 2021. https://www.merritthawkins.com/news-and-insights/blog/lifestyle/the-importance-of-self-care-for-healthcare-professionals-during-COVID-19/.

National Council for Mental Health. 2020. Self-Care Tips for Health Care Workers During COVID-19. Accessed September 2021. http://www.mentalhealthfirstaid.org/2020/04/self-care-tips-for-health-care-workers/.

Panda, M., O'Brien, K.E. & Lo, M.C. 2019. Oath to Self-Care and Well-Being. Accessed May 2021. https://org/10.1016/j.amjmed.2019.10.001.

Soreo. 2021. Self Care Strategies. Accessed March 2021. https://soreo.com/hospice-care/healthcare-providers/self-care-for-healthcare-professionals/.

Chapter Four

Lally, van Jaarsveld, Potts & Wardle. 2009. How are habits formed: Modeling habit formation in the real world. European Journal of Social Psychology, 40(6), 998-1009.

Prochaska, J. O., & DiClemente, C. C. 1982. Transtheoretical therapy: Toward a more integrative model of change. Psychotherapy: Theory, Research & Practice, 19(3), 276–288.

Chapter Six

Kelly. K. 2018. Soul Health: Aligning with Spirit for Radiant Living. North Carolina: Soul Health Press.

National Wellness Institute. 1976. The Six Dimensions of Wellness. Accessed September 2021. https://nationalwellness.org/resources/six-dimensions-of-wellness/.

Chapter Seven

American Psychological Association. 2021. One Year On: Unhealthy Weight Gains, Increased Drinking Reported by Americans Coping with Pandemic Stress. Accessed April 2021. https://www.apa.org/news/press/releases/2021/03/one-year-pandemic-stress.

American Psychological Association. 2021. Slightly More Than 6 in 10 U.S. Adults (61%) Report Undesired Weight Change since Start of Pandemic. Accessed April 2021. https://www.apa.org/news/press.releases/2021/03/march-weight-change.

Lee, B.P., Dodge, J.L, Leventhal, A. & Terrault, N.A. 2020. Retail Alcohol and Tobacco Sales During COVID-19. Accessed March 2021. http://www.acpjournals.org/doi/10.7326/M20-7271.

Lerman, S. E., Eskin, E., Flower, D. J., et. al. 2012. Fatigue risk management in the workplace. Journal of Occupational and Environmental Medicine, 54(2), 231-258.

Panchal, N. et al. 2021. The Implications of COVID-19 for Mental Health and Substance Abuse. Accessed. June 2021. http://www.kff.org/coronavirus-covid-19/issue-brief/the-implications-of-covid-19-for-mental-health-and-substance-use/.

Chapter Eight

Center for the Study of Traumatic Stress. 2020. Recovery and Reintegration for Healthcare Workers Following COVID-19 Surges. Accessed June 2021. https://www.cstonline.org/ assets/media/documents/csts_fs_recovery_and_reintegration_ for_healthcare_workers_following_covid_19_curges.pdf.

Chödrön, P. 2002. Comfortable With Uncertainty: 108 Teachings. Shambala Publications, Inc.

Chödrön, P. 1996. When Things Fall Apart: Heart Advice for Difficult Times. Shambala Publications, Inc.

Clay, R. 2020. COVID-19 and Suicide. Accessed June 2021. https://www.apa.org/monitor/2020/06/covid-suicide.

Compassion Fatigue.org. 2020. What is Compassion Fatigue? Accessed February 2021. http://www.compassionfatigue.org/compassion.html.

Leander, K. Vulnerability, Shame and Health Care. Accessed June 2021. cunninghamgroupins.com/news/vulnerability-shame-and-health-care/.

Legasse, J. 2020. Healthcare Workers Experiencing Burnout, Stress Due to COVID-19 Pandemic. Accessed March 2021. https://healthcarefinancenews.com/newshealthcare-workers-experiencing-burnout-stress-due-covid-19-pandemic.

Lidden, L & Kingerlee, R. 2017. Gender differences in preferences for psychological treatment, coping strategies, and triggers to help-seeking. Accessed March 2021. https://bpspsychub.onlinelibrary.wiley.com/doi/abs/10.1111/bjc.12147.

Nelson, B & Kaminsky, D. 2020. COVID-19's Crushing Mental Health Toll on Health Care Workers. Accessed September 2021. https://www.acsjournals.onlinelibrary.wiley.com/doi /full/10.1002/cncy.22347.

Omnisure Risk Management Consulting. 2020. Suicide Rates Increase During COVID-19, Especially Among Health Care Workers. Accessed July 2021. https://www.Omnisure.comsuicide-rates-increase-during-covid-19-especially-among-healthcare-workers.

Pappa, S, Ntella, V, Giannakas, T, Giannakoulis, VG, Papoutsi, E and Katsaouno P. 2020. Prevalence of depression, anxiety and insomnia among healthcare workers during the COVID-19 pandemic: A systematic review and meta-analysis. Behavioral Immunology. 88: 901-907.

Pietrzak, R.H., Tsai, J, & Southwick, S.M. 2021. Association of Symptoms of Posttraumatic Stress Disorder with Posttraumatic Psychological Growth Among US Veterans During the COVID-19 Pandemic. JAMA Network Open, 4(4).

Poncet, MC, Toullic, P, Papazian, L, et al. 2007. Burnout syndrome in critical care nursing staff. American Journal of Respiratory Critical Care Medicine. 175: 698-704.

Simon, S. Study: Female Healthcare Workers Are Experiencing COVID-19 Burnout at High Rates. 2020. Accessed March 2021. https://www.verywell-health.com/healthcare-worker-burnout-covid-19-female-5096032.

Spencer, J. & Jewett, C. 2021. Twelve Months of Trauma: More Than 3,600 Healthcare Workers Died in Covid's First Year. Accessed July 2021. http://www.us.news/2021/apr/08/us-health-workers-deaths-covid-lost-on-the-frontline.

Talaee, N., Varahram, M., Jamaati, H. et al. 2020. Stress and Burnout in Health Care Workers During COVID-19 Pandemic; Validation of a Questionnaire. Accessed March 2021. https://www.ncbi.nim.nlm.nih.gov/pmc/articles/PMC7275852/.

Chapter Ten
Leander, Katie. 2015. Vulnerability, Shame and Healthcare. Accessed May 2021. https://www.cunninghamgroupins.comnewsvulnerability-shame-and-health-care/.

Rath, Tom. 2010. Wellbeing: The Five Essential Elements. Gallup Press.

Rath, Tom. 2007. Strength Finders 2.0. Gallup Press.

Chapter Eleven
Maxwell, John. 2004. The Journey from Success to Significance. Nashville, Tennessee: Thomas Nelson, Inc.

Wan, W. 2021. Burned Out By the Pandemic, 3 in 10 Health-Care Workers Consider Leaving the Profession. Accessed April 2021. https://www.wash-ingtonpost.com/health/2021/04/22/health-workers-covid-quit.

Worthen, M. 2021. A Once-in-a-Century Crisis Can Help Educate Doctors. Accessed May 2021. https://www.nytimes.com/2021/04/10/opinion/sunday/covid-medical-school-humanities.Html.

Chapter Thirteen
Twist, L. 2017. The Soul of Money: Transforming Your Relationship with Money and Life. W.W. Norton & Company.

Eisenstein, C. 2021. Sacred Economics: Revised: Money, Gift & Society in the Age of Transition. North Atlantic Books.

Keller, K.R. 2020. Op-ed: The Pandemic has Shown that Long-Term Financial Security is a Necessity, not a Luxury. Accessed April 2021. https://www.cnbc.com/2020/10/13/pandemic-shows-long-term-financial-security-is-necessity-not-a-luxury.html.

Kinder, Molly. 2020. Essential but undervalued: Millions of health care workers aren't Getting the pay or respect they deserve in the COVID-19 pandemic. Accessed June 2021. https://www.brookings.edu/research/essential-but-undervalued-millions-of-health-care-workers-arent-getting-the-pay-or-respect-they-deserve-in-the-covid-19-pandemic/.

Lytle, T. 2021. The pandemic alters pay. Accessed May 2021. https://www.shrm.org/hr-today/news/all-things-work/pages/the-pandemic-alters.pay.aspx.

Chapter 14
Bondenman, G. et al. 2010. The association between daily stress and sexual activity. Journal of Family Psychology. 24 (3): 271-9.

Coombe, J., et al. 2021. Love during lockdown: findings from an online survey examining the impact of COVID-19 on the sexual health of people living in Australia. Sexually Transmitted Infection. 97:357–362.

Gray. J. 2005. Mars and Venus in the Bedroom: A Guide to Lasting Romance and Passion. Harper Perennial.

Gray. J. 2005. Mars and Venus on a Date: A Guide for Navigating the 5 Stages of Dating to Create a Loving and Lasting Relationship. Harper Perennial.

Hamilton, L. D. & Meston, C. M. 2013. Chronic stress and sexual function in women. Journal of sexual medicine.

Kamenetz, A. 2020 Childhood Sexual Abuse Reports Are On The Rise Amid Lockdown Order. https://www.npr.org/sections/coronavirus-live-updates/2020/04/28/847251985child-sexual-abuse-reports-are-on-the-rise-amid-lockdown-orders. Accessed July 2021.

Kaszovitz, S. 2021. The Risk of Sexual Assault in the Home During a Pandemic. Accessed June 2021. https://jacksonhealth.org/blog/the-risk-of-sexual-assault-in-the-home-during-a-pandemic/.

Mollaioli D, Sansone A, Ciocca G, et al. 2021. Benefits of Sexual Activity on Psychological, Relational, and Sexual Health During the COVID-19 Breakout. Journal of Sexual Medicine. 18:35–49.

Scott, E. 2020. How stress can cause a low libido. Very Well Mind. Accessed January 2021. www.verywellmind.com/how-stress-can-lead-to-low-libido-3145029.

Chapter Fifteen
Post, S. & Puchalski, C.M. 2000. Physicians and Patient Spirituality: Professional Boundaries, Competency, and Ethics. Annals of Internal Medicine 132: 578: 583.

Puchalski, Christina M. 2001. The Role of Spirituality in Healthcare. Baylor University Medical Center Proceedings. 14: 352:357.

Chapter Sixteen
Expedia.com. 2016. Deprivation Study. Accessed July 2021 https://viewfinder.expedia.com/work-life-imbalance-expedias-2016-vacation-deprivation-study-shows-americans-leave-hundreds-millions-paid-vacation-days-unused/.

Framingham Heart Study. 2007. Accessed April 2012. www.framinghamheart-study.com. Medscape. 2021. Physical Activity at Leisure, Not Work, Tied to Health Benefits. Accessed http://www.medscape.com/viewarticle/949404.

Siegenthaler, L.L. 1997. Health Benefits of Leisure. Parks and Recreation 32 (1): 24-31.

Strauss-Blasche, G. Ekmekcioglu, C, & Marki, W. 2000. Does vacation enable recuperation? Changes in well-being associated with time away from work. Occupational Medicine. 50 (3): 167-172.

Chapter 17
Dossey, L. 2013. One Mind: How Our Individual Mind is Part of a Greater Consciousness and Why it Matters. Hay House, Inc.

ABOUT THE AUTHOR

D
r. Katherine Kelly, PhD, MSPH, is a clinical health psychologist, former Director of Behavioral Science in Family Medicine and medical school professor, best-selling author and speaker.

Dr. Kelly was named "the pioneer of soul health" following the publication of her first book, *Soul Health: Aligning with Spirit for Radiant Living*, which showcased her comprehensive whole health model. Her book gained best-selling status following the release of her second edition. She went on to author another book, *The Recipe for Radiance: Mastering the Art and Soul of Self-Care.*

Her new book, *The Healer's Path to Post-COVID Recovery*, combines her expertise in helping others restore their lives while teaching essential tools for creating a sustainable self-care plan. Dr. Kelly uses her nationally-known holistic health model to help healthcare workers identify the many branches of well-being that were impacted by this life-altering experience, and offers a simple yet meaningful path to reclaiming optimal health.

She has over 34 years of direct client experience and has taught her Soul Health Model to healthcare providers throughout the United States. To learn more or contact Dr. Kelly, visit www.drkatherinetkelly.com.

Made in the USA
Coppell, TX
24 February 2022

74021253R20154